Look before you leap

If you are on the verge of entering this book, with one mighty bound, pause for a moment lest you find yourself in the position of one who's leapt into a bath of hot water, without first dipping the toe, and must bound mightily out again.

First dip your toe into these preliminary pages of soothing explanations, and then plunge on. It won't render the water any less hot but at least you'll be prepared for the shock.

You'll find large sections of the book devoted to the antics of a boy and his dog or, as the dog would have it, a dog and his boy. Boon companions, they. Facing whatever the world may throw at them (whatever it is the boy will hurl it back if the dog doesn't scoff it first) yet there is a constant tussle twixt the pair as to who leads and who follows.

Wellington, the boy (named after his own footwear), assumes the mantle of leadership by virtue of being a fully-paid-up member of the human race. Boot, the dog, dismisses such simplistic reasoning; pointing out that Wellington hasn't even learned to locomote on all fours - and lurches from crisis to disaster in constant danger of toppling. Moreover Boot refuses to be treated like any common canine since he believes himself to be an eighteenth century nobleman, conjured into this perplexing century and a voluminous hairy skin by the curse of a gipsy wench whom he crossed in love, whilst omitting to cross her palm with silver.

Wellington ripostes with the claim that he does all the brainwork, an activity he can be seen engaged in at the top of the page, but Boot regards as derisory the appellation 'Brain' to a mechanism which seems to function only in the horizontal mode.

Wellington presses his claim by declaring he's the provider for the duo, but Boot thinks nature has quite properly provided the Wellingtons of this world for the sole purpose of providing, free of charge, for those of more elevated rank - and wishes the lad would stop pursuing him with the wretched bill.

The pursuit of happiness

A glance at the top of this page will reveal a scene which you could be forgiven for thinking depicts a sackful of old army boots grappling with an unspecified lump. However a more diligent scrutiny will reveal an attempt to portray a girl, Maisie by name, in pursuance of a boy called Marlon.

Marlon is the object of Maisie's affections, but just why is difficult to define. Is it his woolly manner, his raving hair, his lack of couth, his wandering gait or the winsome eccentricity of housing his brain in his boots? None of these. Maisie knows full well the object of her desire is a stupid lump; but he's the only stupid lump available and she's not about to see him snapped up by some brazen hussy whose only interest in the lad is the bit of fluff-gathering toffee lurking in a pocket of his donkey-jacket.

Marlon does not reciprocate Maisie's affections. For one thing he doesn't know what reciprocate means. And if he did know, he couldn't do it. It's a manoeuvre beyond the scope of one who has to have FRONT printed on the front of his constantly-worn racing overalls - so he'll know in which direction to point himself. Moreover if he did have an inkling of its meaning he'd run a mile, whereas at present he runs only half a mile - whenever Maisie appears.

But Maisie remains undaunted, continuing to chase her dream (they don't come any dreamier than Marlon) and make any sacrifice; in evidence of which we show her in the act of sharing her last sandwich with her beloved.

A bundle of joy

Some years ago Maisie's mother went off for a short stay in hospital, promising her daughter she'd return with a soft and cuddly surprise. Maisie was sure this was going to be the puppy for which she'd been petitioning but when, subsequently, the gift-wrapped surprise was presented and unwrapped it turned out to be a baby brother – just what Maisie didn't want and has wanted less and less as the years have gone by.

However, Maisie is bound to the sibling by a stern sense of duty, filial bonds, and her mother's promise of a thick ear if she doesn't look after the little angel and keep him out of mischief.

If Maisie's mum diligently carried out her threats Maisie would by now have ears as big as those of elephants. Baby Grumpling, for such is his name, doesn't need to get into mischief – he himself is mischief personified. Not that he is by nature ill-intentioned. On the contrary he has devoted his life to helping mankind in its constant struggle to achieve total anarchy. Such worthwhile inventions as the Polyfilla blancmange, the spider in the bath (and the bed, and the underwear drawer, and Maisie's tights) the worm sandwich, the glue-on-the-loo and other aids to gracious living, too numerous to list, can be accredited to Maisie's little brother.

As an aid to identification and subsequent evasive action, he is here depicted in two situations. Top left he can be seen enjoying the special slimmers' version of his celebrated worm sandwich, having discarded the bread, and lower down you see him answering a theological question from Maisie ("For God's sake what are you up to now?") by pointing to a higher authority; although, considering his life-style, he should perhaps be pointing down.

LOOK MARLON - YOU'RE NOT SPOSED TO BOUNCE ON THE BOUNCER WITH THE HEAD - Y'DO IT WITH THE FEET
FRONT
U222

Y'SEE - THE FEET MARLON
JUMP IN ON THE FEET

OH VERY GOOD - BUT I DIN'T ACTUALLY MEAN ON MY FEET
Maurice Dodd

GET OFF, MARLON - GET OFF
HEE HEE-HEE
ROWF ROWF
U223

YOU'RE A RIGHT CLOWN, MARLON IN FAC' YOU'RE JUS' ABOUT THE BIGGEST CLOWN I KNOW
HEE - HEE-HEE HEE
ROWF ROWF

MIND YOU - I WOULDN'T WANT ANYBODY TO FEEL LEFT OUT
HEEE - HEE-HEE-HEE HEEEEE
ROWF ROWF
Maurice Dodd

the Perishers OMNIBUS
WHAT D'YOU THINK OF CASTLE LIFE ?
OVER-INFLATED IF YOU ASK ME
By Maurice Dodd · Mirror Publications

First published in Great Britain in 1988 by
Mirror Publications Ltd., Irwin House,
118 Southwark Street, London SE1 OSW.
Printed and bound in Great Britain by
Spottiswoode Ballantyne Ltd., Colchester and
London. Distribution by IPC Magazines,
Circulation Sales and Distribution, London.

ISBN 1 85386 139 1

WHAT'S GOIN' ON?
WHAT'RE YOU FOOLS UP TO?
IT'S A BOUNCER MAISIE
IT'S GREAT FOR EXERCISE
-TONES UP THE MUSCLES - IMPROVES CIRCULATION -BURNS OFF FAT
YAWN
-AN' IT DOESN' HALF WORK UP AN APPETITE
I TRUST YOU'VE LAID ON SOMETHIN' SUBSTANTIAL FOR AFTERWARDS
U224
Maurice Dodd

LISTEN MAISIE - I SAID BOUNCIN' WORKED UP AN APPETITE
THAT WASN' AN INVITATION TO GUZZLE MY SCOFF
YOU GOT ME UP THERE ON FALSE PRETENTIONS
YOU'VE GOT MY MUSCLES TONED LIKE MAD - MY BLOOD'S SEETHIN' ABOUT - I'VE WORKED UP A GINORMOUS APPETITE AN' YOU WON'T EVEN GIVE ME A BITE
OH CRUMBS YOU C'N HAVE THE FREE RUN OF MY LARDER
HEY WHAT'RE YOU DOIN' - YOU'LL WORK UP AN EVEN BIGGER APPETITE
IF I'M COMPETIN' WITH A LARDER I'M GOIN' FOR THE GOLD
U225
FRONT
Maurice Dodd

I CAN'T WAIT TO GET INTO YOUR LARDER, WELLIN'TON -I'VE GOT AN APPETITE LIKE A HORSE
YEA-AN' THE FACE TO MATCH, TOO
-A PACKET OF CHOC'LATE BISCUITS
IN FAC' IT'S A WONDER YOU'VE NEVER GONE IN FOR 'HORSE OF THE YEAR'
A TIN OF PEACHES
OR IF YOU WERE REALLY AMBITIOUS.. -HERE-WHAT'S ALL THIS BISCUITS AN' PEACHES STUFF?
IT'S WHAT EACH OF THOSE REMARKS WILL COST YOU
CARE TO RISK ANOTHER THROW OF THE DICE?
Maurice Dodd
U226

HERE WE ARE AT YOUR LARDER, WELLIN'TON
WHERE YOU SAID I COULD MAKE MYSELF AT HOME
FRONT
P'RHAPS I SHOULD DO A LITTLE MORE LIMBERIN' UP BEFORE I GET STUCK IN
HUP-TWO-THREE -HUP...
WELL GOOD LUCK, WELLINTON I'LL BE LEAVIN' YOU NOW
CRUMBS, MARLON-I HAVEN'T UPSET YOU TOO?
NO-IT'S JUS THAT I CAN'T STAN RE-RUNS
AN' I'VE ALREADY SEEN 'JAW'S'
Maurice Dodd
U227

OK, WELLIN'TON-
YOU SAID I COULD HELP MYSELF IN YOUR LARDER
SO LET ME AT IT!
TA-RAH ♫
THOUGH I MUS' WARN YOU OF THE POSSIBILITY OF DISAPPOINTMENT WITH SOME ASPECTS
BUT THERE ARE FEATURES TO BE MUCH ADMIRED
IT'S EMPTY!
-YOU WILL HAVE ALREADY NOTED THE SPECTACULAR ECHO EFFECT
EMPTY EMPTY EMPTY EMPTY
Maurice Dodd
U228

WELLIN'TON-
YOU SAID I C'D HAVE A BIG SCOFF IN YOUR LARDER AN' THERE'S NOTHIN' IN THERE!
NO-NO MAISIE-I SAID YOU C'D HAVE THE FREE RUN OF MY LARDER
I SAID NAUGHT OF ITS CONTENTS
U229
SO I SPAKE NOT A WORD OF UNTRUTH
THOUGH I WILL ADMIT TO A SLIGHT DISSEMBLANCE
Maurice Dodd
-THERE'S NOT A LOT OF ROOM IN THERE FOR RUNNIN'
AN' YOU NEED TO RUN NOT MERELY FOR THE EXERCISE
'COS IF YOU DON'T RUN ALL THE WAY HOME YOU'LL MISS YOUR TEA!

WELL WE HAD GREAT FUN WITH MAISIE BUT THE TRUTH IS, BOOT, THE LARDER IS EMPTY
AN' IT BEIN' RIGHT AFTER THE HOLIDAY I'M JUST ABOUT SKINT
WE'LL HAVE TO THROW OURSELVES ON THE MERCY OF BEN-THE-BUTCHER IN THE HIGH STREET
AN' A KINDER, NOBLER, MORE GENEROUS PERSON I HAVE YET TO MEET
CRUMBS- THAT'S THE FIRST TIME I'VE HAD TO LEAVE A DEPOSIT ON A SAUSAGE!
Maurice Dodd
U230

WE'VE GOT TO FIND SOME WAY OF RAISIN' FUNDS, BOOT

I'VE GOT IT!
-A CAR- BOOT SALE!

IT'S SURE FIRE
PEOPLE WILL BUY JUST ABOUT ANYTHIN' FROM A CAR BOOT
U231
Maurice Dodd

NOW-AS TO THE PRACTICAL DETAILS
THE FIRST THING WE NEED IS A CAR

CRUMBS- IT'S TYPICAL INNIT?
I HAVE THE BRILLIANT IDEA OF A CAR-BOOT SALE AN' IMMEDIATELY SNIT A HAG
I MEAN HIT A SNAG
-MAYBE I C'N GET SOMEBODY TO **LEND** ME A CAR
MauriceDodd
I'LL WRITE TO THOSE TWO BLOKES IN THE CAR-TRADE
YOU KNOW -THINGEY AN' WOTSIT
U232
AH-HANG ABOUT, WAIT A MO'-THIS COULD BE A PROBLEM
WHICH ONE SHALL I ADDRESS FIRST- ROLLS OR ROYCE?

CRUMBS- NOW I'VE HIT ANOTHER SNAG
IF I WRITE TO ROLLS AN' ROYCE -TO LEN' ME A CAR FOR MY CAR-BOOT SALE
WHICH ONE-SHALL I ADDRESS FIRST?
IT'S A MATTER OF PROTOCOL REALLY
U233
-AN' I DON'T WANT THEM FALLIN' OUT OVER ME
MauriceDodd

WHILE I'M WRITIN' TO ROLLS AND ROYCE I MIGHT AS WELL PUT THE BITE ON A FEW MORE PROSPECTS
U234
THERES THAT BLOKE WITH THE BAND-THE ONE WHO GOT A MEDAL. HE MANAGED TO RAISE A FEW BOB
"DEAR MR BAND-AID, I'VE BEEN USIN' YOUR STICKIN-PLASTER SINCE..."
Maurice Dodd
AN' THERE'S THAT MR MAXWELL-HE SHOULD BE GOOD FOR A TOUCH
"DEAR MR MAXWELL-AS A LONG-TIME DRINKER OF YOUR COFFEE..."
YOU'LL NOTICE THESE CRAFTY LITTLE TOUCHES I'M PUTTIN' IN, BOOT
IT HELPS TO GET 'EM ON YOUR SIDE

I DIDN'T GET AN ANSWER FROM MR ROLLS OR MR ROYCE
THEY MUST'VE GOT MY LETTER
I PUT A FIRST-CLASS STICKY MARK WHERE THE STAMP SHOULD'VE BEEN
-SO IT WOULD LOOK AS IF IT HAD FALLEN OFF IN THE POST
WELL-IT LOOKS AS IF I'M NOT GOIN' TO GET A CAR FOR MY CAR-BOOT SALE
SO BE IT
WHO NEEDS THEIR ROTTEN OLE CAR, ANYWAY?
WELLINGTON BOOT SALE
Maurice Dodd
U235

SEE ANYTHIN' YOU FANCY?
W-E-L-L -I MIGHT TAKE THAT ROTTEN OLE PENCIL OFF YOUR HAN'S
LLINGTON BOOT SALE
Maurice Dodd
ROTTEN OLE...? LISTEN-THERE'S MILES OF SCRIBBLIN' LEFT IN THIS
BUT SINCE I'M DESPERATE YOU C'N HAVE IT FOR 2p HOW ABOUT THAT?
N
U236
HMMM-WELL, IT'S A GOOD START
-NOW-LET'S HAGGLE
ON

NOW SEE WHAT YOU'VE MADE ME DO -I'VE SNAPPED THE PENCIL
ALL COS YOU WANT TO HAGGLE OVER 2p
CRUMBS- I COULDN'T BE SO MEAN
WELLINGTON BOOT SALE
Maurice Dodd
-AN' THAT'S PRECISELY WHY YOU'RE NOT A MILLIONAIRE
AS- IT HAPPENS- NEITHER ARE YOU A MILLIONAIRE
ON
WELL I'VE BEEN VERY BUSY LATELY
U237
BUT AS SOON AS I C'N GET ROUN' TO IT....
ON

WELL I DON'T SPOSE THERES ANYTHIN' ELSE IN THAT BOOTFUL OF OLE RUBBISH OF INTEREST TO ME
DON'T BE SO HASTY
Maurice Dodd
U238
I HAVE HERE A GENUINE ALMOS'-AS-GOOD-AS-SECON' HAN' IMITATION SWISS ARMY KNIFE
IT'S STILL GOT ONE UNBROKEN BLADE, A BOTTLE OPENER A THING FOR TAKIN' STONES OUT OF HORSES' HOOVES
BUT MOST OF ALL (AN' IT MIGHT'VE BEEN DESIGNED WITH YOU EXCLUSIVELY IN MIND)
THERE'S A DEVICE FOR GRINDIN' THE FACES OF THE POOR!
BOOT
SALE

U239
ANYTHIN' THERE YOU FANCY?
WOT'S THAT THING FOR?
THAT? OH, THAT'S WHAT'S KNOWN AS A, ER... STICK
IT'S FOR UM..FOR PRODDIN' THINGS
COR-THERE'S HOURS 'N' HOURS OF CREATIVE PRODDIN' THERE
TELL YOU WHAT-YOU C'N HAVE IT FOR A PENNY
OW ABOUT EASY TERMS?
WELL- I DON'T THINK 'STUPID GREAT LUMP' IS VERY NICE
IT WAS THE EASIEST TERM I COULD BRING TO MIND
Maurice Dodd

AH- DIRTY McSQUIRTY
I'VE GOT THE VERY THING FOR YOU
WELLINC BOOT SALE
Maurice Dodd
U240
A FLY WHISK
HERE- GIVE IT A TEST-RUN
HAVE A FREE WHISK ON ME
-NO THANKS
IT MAKES THEM FAR TOO EXCITABLE

U241
AH- FISCAL YERE
WELLINGI BOOT SALE
Maurice Dodd

YOU LOOK LIKE A DISCERNIN' SHOPPER....

PRECISELY

AH- BABY GRUMPLIN'
I KNOW I'VE GOT SOMETHIN' TO INTEREST YOU
THIS SUPER WIN'MILL
WELLINGTON BOOT SALE
IT GOES LIKE MAD
IF YOU BLOW HARD
WELL- REALLY HARD
WITH THIS LI'L NUMBER YOU'LL BE THE ENVY OF THE WIN'MILL- OWNIN' CLASSES
I'M BEGINNIN' TO WONDER IF I'M REALLY SUITED TO THE CUT-AN'-THRUST OF TRADIN'
Maurice Dodd
U242

OH I DON'T KNOW WHY I'VE BEEN TRYIN' TO FLOG ALL THIS TAT
I'VE JUS' NOT BEEN THINKIN' STRAIGHT
I SHOULD BE EXPLOITIN' MY NATURAL TALENT
WELLINGTON BOOT SALE
AFTER ALL I'M A WRITER OF NO MEAN ABILITY
I'LL SELL MY SKILL AN' EXPERTISE TO OTHERS
BY STARTIN' A CORRESPONDENCE COURSE
I'LL PUT AN AD IN THE LOCAL SHOP
THEY MIGHT DO IT FOR FREE
NOW, LEMME SEE...'THE ART OF THE BEGGIN' LETTER...'
Maurice Dodd
U243

maisie?
Maurice Dodd

are you sitting on mi worms?

don't move- don't move-you'll damage them even more
U244

i'll have to find a way to lever you up and-oh, wait, hang about

it's all right-they're over here
-you must be sitting on mi spiders

i think you're sitting on mi spiders
AAGH

that's funny-they're not here
oh, crumbs
Maurice Dodd

i hope they haven't crept into your tights
AAAGH
coo, maisie, i wish i was able to do that

-run up the wall
AAAGH
AAAGH
AAAGH
U245

crumbs maisie there's no need to go on like that
AAAGH
couldn't you be a little more constructive?
AAAGH
i only said i thought mi spiders had crawled into your tights
AAAGH
however - on closer examination...
U246
Maurice Dodd

crumbs, maisie -just because i thought mi spiders were in your tights there was no need for you to strip off
and i wish you'd act with a little more decorum
i was sure i'd left those spiders on the chair where you were sitting
but i didn't-so i wonder where...
AAAAGH
ah-yes-now i remember
U247
Maurice Dodd

I'LL GET YOU FOR TELLING ME I HAD SPIDERS IN MY TIGHTS, BABY GRUMPLIN' -YOU SEE IF I DON'T
you'll have to get past 'samson' first
he's mi special minder spider
he's big 'n' rough 'n' tough-he only just fits into this matchbox
WELL, SAMSON -MEET DELILAH
TAKE THAT 'N' THAT 'N' THAT 'N' THAT
he's not called samson for nothing
GRR
Maurice Dodd
U248

AAGH-GETIMOFF GETIMOFF!
that's easier said than done
you've infuriated him
GRR
'samson' doesn't take kindly to being jumped on
but you might be able to buy him off with a bit of choc'late
GRR
OH..... VERY WELL THEN
GRR

thanks, maisie
as his agent i get 75%
glop
Maurice Dodd
U249

SMASH
SMASH
SMASH
SMASH
SMASH
U250

caught you, maisie!
smashing up the matchbox i keep samson mi pet spider in
-just as well i was taking him for a walk
GRR
Maurice Dodd

U251

samson and me want a **word** with you!
GRR
Maurice Dodd

BANG
LAST GASP
U252

SPLASH

CRUNCH

BITE
Maurice Dodd

I'M HERE TO SPREAD THE GOOD NEWS
THERE WILL BE GREAT JOY AMONGST YOU ON SATURDAY
A DAY OF NASHNUL REJOICIN'
D'YOU WANT TO KNOW WHY?
'COS THERE'S JOY IN GIVIN' -THAT'S WHY
'TIS BETTER TO GIVE THAN TO RECEIVE
AN' SINCE IT HAPPENS TO BE MY BIRTHDAY...
OI -HANG ABOUT-I HAVEN'T FINISHED SPREADIN'
U253
Maurice Dodd

ABOUT MY BIRTHDAY TOMORROW
CRUMBS, WELLIN'TON-WE HOPE YOU'RE NOT GOIN' TO GO RABBITIN' ON ABOUT PRESENTS
U254
WELL WHAT'S WRONG IN HOPIN' FOR A FEW PRESENTS?
IT'S NOT SO MUCH THE GIFTS - I JUS' WANNA BE REMEMBERED
WELL, WE COULD REMEMBER YOU WITHOUT GIVIN' YOU PRESENTS
IS THAT THE WAY YOU WANT TO REMEMBER ME?
UNDERPRIVILEGED - DESOLATE - DESTITUTE BROKEN ON LIFE'S WHEEL....
MauriceDodd

WELL HERE WE ARE ON THE GREAT DAY - OCTOBER 25
THE ANNIVERSARY OF THE BATTLE OF AGINCOURT
AN' IT'S A SAINT'S DAY - ST CRISPIN - THE PATRON SAINT OF POTATO CHIPS
IT ALSO HAPPENS TO BE MY BIRTHDAY
U255
UP TO NOW I'VE HAD ONE CARD
AN' I SENT THAT TO MYSELF
I DIDN'T EVEN POST IT - I SLIPPED IT UNDER THE DOOR
MauriceDodd
CRUMBS - I DIN'T THINK I COULD BE SO MEAN

WELL, BOOT, YOU COULD SAY I HAD A GOOD BIRTHDAY-AS BIRTHDAYS GO
A CARD FLOODED IN FROM MAISIE AN' MARLON
THEY WENT HALVES IN IT
AN' THAT'S HOW THEY SENT IT-A SEPARATE HALF EACH!
U256
DIRTY Mc SQUIRTY GAVE ME A 3p GIFT VOUCHER-FOR THE OXFAM SHOP
I GOT A LICKED-AN'-APPROVED-WINE GUM FROM BABY GRUMPLIN'
AN' FROM FISCAL YERE SOME SOUN' ADVICE ON HOW TO INVEST A THOUSAN' POUNDS
-FILLED WITH THE SKIMMED-MILK OF HUMAN KINDNESS
-A DAY TO REMEMBER
Maurice Dodd

bad news, maisie, bad news
mi pet spider samson
-he's escaped
OH DEAR. BABY GRUMPLIN' -THAT'S TERRIBLE
Maurice Dodd
U257
mind you -there are aspects i find puzzling
he opened his box from the inside -turned on the lights ate two sweets -opened mi bedroom door..
then unlocked the front door
WELL-YOU SAID YOURSELF -HE'S A VERY CLEVER SPIDER
-but-not clever enough to do joined up writing!
This is a breakout -goodbye
Samson

you let mi spider escape and you wrote this note as well
NO-NO- I MEAN YES-YES- I-MOAN-OH- AAAH
I COULD'N' HELP IT-HE MADE ME DO IT-HE HELD A PISTOL TO MY HEAD
a pistol? a pistol? is that likely-where would a spider get a pistol?
AH-ER- ALL RIGHT YOU WIN
IT WAS PROBABLY A FAKE– BUT I WAS'N' THINKIN' CLEARLY AT THE TIME
U258
Maurice Dodd

it was totally irresponsible of you maisie, letting mi spider escape
i think maybe i should inform the police
OH CRUMBS, BABY GRUMPLIN' (SIGH)
D'YOU REALLY THINK THE P'LICE ARE GOIN' TO SPEND TIME SEARCHIN' FOR A SPIDER?
that wasn't what i had in mind
i was thinking more of them searching for the victims
Maurice Dodd
U259

G'MORNING-
I'M POOR-
GIRL
I COME
FROM A VERY
POOR FAMILY
U260
I KNOW
ALL ABOUT
YOUR FAMILY
YOUR MOTHER'S
POOR-YOUR FATHER'S
POOR-YOUR MAID'S POOR
YOUR BUTLER'S POOR-I'VE
HEARD IT ALL BEFORE
Maurice Dodd
OH-A
KNOW-ALL,
A?
WELL LET
ME TELL YOU,
YOU DON'T KNOW
AS MUCH AS
YOU THINK
YOU LEFT
OUT THE
KENNEL-
MAID

... AND THERE'S
OUR IMPOVERISHED
CHAUFFEUR-HE
C'N HARDLY AFFORD
THE POLISH FOR
THE ROLLS...
YOU'RE
WASTIN' YOUR
TIME TELLIN'
ME ALL THIS-
I'M BROKE
Maurice Dodd
U261
HANG ABOUT
LET ME SEE IF
I'VE GOT THE
RIGHT PERSON
HERE...
WELLINGTON
BOOT ESQ-IS
THAT YOU?
AS A
MATTER
O'FAC'
-NO
I'M WELLIN'TON,
HE'S BOOT THERE'S
TWO OF US
OH, GOOD-
THAT'S
DOUBLE THE
CONTRIBUTION

RIGHT-THAT'S A DOUBLE CONTRIBUTION FROM WELLINGTON, BOOT & CO...
U262

....PROFITS IN EXCESS OF ONE MILLION PER ANNUM
Maurice Dodd

PROFITS IN EXCESS OF...?
WHERE DID YOU GET THAT RUBBISHY LIST?

FROM THE STONEYBROKE BUSINESS INFORMATION BUREAU
THEY'RE VERY ECONOMICAL TO USE-'COS WE ONLY PAY THEM BY RESULTS

LISTEN-NOT ONLY DO WE NOT MAKE A PROFIT IN EXCESS OF ONE MILLION
WE MAKE NO PROFIT AT ALL

WE'VE GOT A PERMANENT CASH-FLOW PROBLEM
THERE'S NO CASH AN' NO FLOW

THERE'S NO NEED TO BE EMBARRASSED ABOUT CASH AVAILABILITY
Maurice Dodd

I'LL TAKE - DINERS, ACCESS, AMERICAN EXPRESS, MASTERCARD...
U263

I'M NOT SPENDING ALL MY TIME BEING POOR JUST TO BE BILKED BY THE LIKES OF YOU
Maurice Dodd
U264
I KEEP TELLIN' YOU-I'M POORER THAN YOU ARE-I'M SKINT, FLAT, BUSTED, BROKE
OH YEA? LET'S HAVE A LOOK IN YOUR POCKETS!
GEROFF LEGGO
ARF
ARF
NOTHING-THERES NOTHING IN YOUR POCKETS!
WAIT A MINUTE-WHAT'VE YOU GOT IN YOUR HAT?
MY HEAD
HMM... I COULD GET A VALUATION..

LISTEN, POOR-GIRL, THERE'S NOTHIN' I C'N GIVE YOU
I'M BROKE-BUST-YOUR AVERAGE STONE IS RICH IN CORPUSCLES WHEN COMPARED TO ME
Maurice Dodd
THERE'S NO NEED TO GET UP-TIGHT
YOU SOUND IN NEED OF A HOLIDAY TO ME
I C'N FIX YOU UP WITH A SPECIAL ECONOMY DEAL
HOW ABOUT OUR OFF-PEAK TANNERY TOUR?
OR THE TIP-TREK WEEKEND
OR THE SEWAGE PLANT SAFARI?
YOU WON'T GET MANY OFFERS LIKE THESE
IT'S ONLY 'COS MY UNCLE OWNS THE ALTERNATIVE-LIFE-STYLE TRAVEL AGENCY
U265

KNOCK KNOCK
AAAAGH
U266
SLAM
ER.. BABY GRUMPLIN'? YOUR AH, SPIDER'S COME BACK (GULP)
samson? coo-he'll jump for joy when he sees me
I WOULDN'T **COUNT** ON IT

samson- mi pet spider- where is he?
HE'S AT THE DOOR
WELL, STRIC'LY SPEAKIN'-HE'S MORE LIKE, **IN** THE DOOR
U267
well don't just stand there -open up
ER...RIGHT - THE THING IS, BABY GRUMPLIN', YOU'LL FIND HE'S KIND OF... *CHANGED*
FOR ONE THING HE'S **SLIMMED DOWN** QUITE A BIT
FLOP

samson-
mi very best
spider...
you've
flattened
him
IT WAS
AN ACCIDENT
HONES'LY,
BABY
GRUMPLIN'
I'D DO
ANYTHIN' TO
BRING HIM
BACK TO YOU
ANYTHIN'
ANYANY
ANYANY
ANYTHIN'
right then
-administer
the kiss
of life
A?WHAT?
EEEUGH!
-HANG
ABOUT
what
d'you think
you're
doing?
I THOUGHT
THE PROD OF LIFE
WOULD BE MUCH
MORE EFFECTIVE
U268
Maurice Dodd

accident or
not-you killed
mi spider, maisie
and for
that the king
of the spiders
will come and
get you in
the night
THE KING OF
THE SPIDERS-THE
KING OF THE
SPIDERS...
WHAT
KING OF THE
SPIDERS?
the king of
the spiders who's
ten feet tall and
covered with ginger
hair and has teeth
like a chain-saw
OH-THAT
KING OF THE
SPIDERS
U269
Maurice Dodd

THE KING OF THE SPIDERS
THERE IS NO KING OF THE SPIDERS
AN' GOBBLES YOU UP
JUS' 'COS YOU KILLED A SPIDER
WHAT RUBBISH
WHAT COMES IN THE NIGHT
IT'S THAT ROTTEN BABY GRUMPLIN'S IDEA OF A JOKE
ER.. BABY GRUMPLIN'-AHA.. AHA-HA...HA
Y'DON'T REALLY THINK THE KING OF THE SPIDERS IS COMIN'-DO YOU?
well i'm not expecting santa-claus
Maurice Dodd
U270

WELL HE DIDN'T COME DID HE?
THE KING OF THE SPIDERS
IN SPITE OF ALL YOUR STUPID THREATS AN' WARNIN'S HE DIDN'T COME
y'mean he didn't come to you
i saved you by leaving the drink and sandwiches
OH, COME ON, BABY GRUMPLIN', YOU SCOFFED THAT NOSH YOU KNOW YOU DID
crumbs, maisie, you've guessed mi secret
swallowing a dozen large fly sarnies and a quart of stout at bedtime gives me mi youthful looks
Maurice Dodd
U271

WELL I RECKON THIS IS DEAD STUPID-HAVIN' A FUNERAL FOR A SPIDER
YEA-ME TOO
LOOK IT'S ONLY TO KEEP BABY GRUMPLIN' HAPPY
IT'S A GAME-JUST A GAME
DON'T TAKE IT SO SERIOUS...
Maurice Dodd U272
...LY
right then-who can whistle the dead march from 'saul'?

wellington, you've got a way with words
would you say a few over the grave?
OH, AH... VERY WELL THEN, BABY GRUMPLIN'
U273
ER...WE'RE GATHERED TO MOURN THE PASSIN' OF SAMSON
A SPIDER OF MANY, ER, ACCOMPLISHMENTS .... AN' EIGHT LEGS
WHO E'EN NOW IS ENJOYIN' HIS REWARD IN THE GREAT WEB IN THE SKY
SCOFFIN' BIG JUICY FLIES AN'..
I WAS HOPING THIS WOULD BE A NON-CONTROVERSIAL FUNERAL
Maurice Dodd

well goodbye samson- noblest spider of them all
BOO-HOO
BOO-HOO-HOO-HOO HOOO
U274

WAAAAH AAGH, OOOH, BOOO-HOOOO-HOOOOOOOOO
CRUMBS, I CAN'T STAN' HYPOCRISY
OH-I'M THE SAME
EXCEP' WHEN IT'S MEANT SINCERELY
Maurice Dodd

'LO, BOOT
D'YOU KNOW WHERE I'VE BEEN?
Maurice Dodd

TO A FUNERAL-A SPIDER'S FUNERAL
COULD YOU IMAGINE ME DOIN' ANYTHIN' SO DAFT?
U275
OH, EASILY -QUITE EASILY

WHERE THE MIND JIBS IS IN ATTEMPTING TO ENVISAGE YOU DOING ANYTHING SENSIBLE

WELL?
U276

WELL HOW DID YOU GET ON?
FRONT

SLAM

STATIONERY CUPBOARD
LOOK-ALL I WANT TO KNOW IS DID WE WIN OR LOSE?

ER, MAR-LON ♫
YEA. MAISIE? (VROOM VROOM)
DON'T YOU FEEL LIFE IS PASSIN' US BY?
I MEAN- ALL MY FRIENDS HAVE PROPER BOY-FRIENDS (TEE-HEE)
WELL SO HAVE I -THERE'S WELLIN'TON AN THERE'S...
NO-NO, KISSY-FACE- I'M TALKIN' ABOUT FRIENDS OF THE OPPOSITE SEX
OW, WELL -I DON'T KNOW ABOUT THAT
I DON'T THINK WELLIN'TON WOULD WANT TO CHANGE
U277

MARLON – I'M BEGINNIN' TO THINK YOU'RE PECULIAR
Maurice Dodd U278
YOU COULD HAVE THIS 'ERE FAB FEMALE FOR YOUR VERY OWN!
TO HAVE AN' TO HOLD AN' HOLD AN' HOLD (GISSAKISS) AN' HOLD
COR-I'D MAKE A MAN OF YOU
I'LL MAKE Y'R BLOOD BOIL Y'R EYES POP Y'R HAIR CURL AN' Y'R BREATH COME IN SHORT UNDERWEAR
CRUMBS, MAISIE - AN' YOU THINK I'M PECULIAR

LISTEN, MARLON· WHEN I SAID YOU SHOULD HAVE A FRIEND OF THE OPPOSITE SEX...
I WASN' TALKIN' ABOUT WELLIN'TON CHANGIN'
I WAS TALKIN' ABOUT ME
OW-YEA- I SEE WOT YOU MEAN
AN' THINK IT'D SUIT YOU
BUT I DON'T THINK THEY DO IT ON THE NASHNUL 'EALTH
Maurice Dodd U279

C'MON 'EARTBREAKER, GISSAKISS?
YEUK
'ELP
AAGH
HEY- THAT'S MY BES' FRIEN'
GET YOUR HAN'S OFF MY BES' FRIEN'
I GOTTER HAVE A MAN-D'YOU HEAR ME-IF I CAN'T HAVE THIS ONE I'LL HAVE WHATEVER COMES ALONG
IN WHICH CASE I HAVE NO HESITATION IN RECOMMENDIN' MY BES' FRIEN'
Maurice Dodd
U280

OH-OH- I'M AT YOUR MERCY -GISSAKISS
SQUIRP SQUIRP
'ELP, WELLIN'TON, 'ELP
NAUGHT CAN WITHSTAN' A WOMAN IN LOVE -GISSAKISS
SQUIRP SQUIRP
DON' LEAVE ME-WHAT KIND OF A FRIEN' ARE YOU?
SQUIRP SQUIRP SQUIRP
THE SORT OF FRIEN' YOU C'N ABSOLUTELY RELY ON... FOR SOME WELL-CONSIDERED ADVICE
Maurice Dodd
U281

C'MON' MARLON, GISSAKISS Y'DON'T KNOW WHAT YOU'RE MISSIN'
YEUK-GERROFF I KNOW 'XACLY WOT I'M MISSIN'
KISSIN' WEAKENS A MAN-IT KILLED MY UNCLE
KILLED BY KISSIN'?
YEA-'E WAS ALWAYS CHASIN' WOMEN
BUT 'E AD TO DRINK TWO BOTTLES OF RUM A DAY
TO OVERCOME 'IS SHYNESS
BUT WHAT DID HE DIE OF?
IT'S OBVEROUS INNIT?
CHASIN' WOMEN AT 98 WAS TOO MUCH FOR 'IM
U282
Maurice Dodd
I DUNNO WHY I'VE BEEN THROWIN' MYSELF AT YOU-YOU STUPID LUMP
I'VE GIVEN YOU THE BES' YEARS OF MY LIFE
O'COURSE -THAT'S NOT QUITE TRUE
THE BES' YEARS OF MY LIFE ARE GOIN' TO BE WHEN I'M A BEAUTIFUL AN' TALENTED LADY PEST EXTERNIMATOR
-AN' INTERNASHNUL POP-STAR
I'LL HAVE DIAMON'S AN' FURS AN' STUFF
AN' THE PICK OF THE WORL'S MOST HAN'SOME MEN
AN' I'LL HAVE A NEW DOLLY'S PRAM AN' A DOLLY'S TEA-SET AN' A BOX OF SMARTIES AN'...
Maurice Dodd
U283

MEN..
I'M FINISHED WITH MEN
Maurice Dodd

I HATE MEN

NOTHIN'S TOO BAD FOR MEN
hullo maisie

mum- maisie bit mi balloon!
U284

I'VE FINISHED WITH MEN
YEA- ME TOO
Maurice Dodd

I HATE MEN
YEA- ME TOO
EXCEP' OF COURSE FOR Y'R DAD

I MEAN- IF IT WEREN'T FOR YOUR FATHER YOU WOULDN' BE HERE
YEA- THA'S RIGHT

WE'D STILL BE AT 27 ACCACIA AVENUE -I LIKED IT THERE
U285

USIN' THE ACCUMULATED CUNNIN' OF WOMEN THROUGH THE AGES
AN' JUST A FEW AIDS TO MY OWN NATURAL ATTRACTIONS
AN' SAND -I'VE GOT TO HAVE SOME SAND
I WON'T GIVE IN- I'LL FIGHT FOR MY MAN
.....EYE BLACK, PERFUME -SPRAY, MUM'S STOCKIN'S
♪
SSSSSSS
WHOP
Maurice Dodd U286
WHA HAPPENED- WHA' HAPPENED?
LE'S JUS' SAY YOU WERE STRUCK BY LOVE

CRUMBS. MARLON- WHAT A GAME!
WHAT WITH THE GOAL COLLAPSIN'!
AN THE REF BITIN' THE LINESMAN'S GUIDE-DOG!
MIND YOU I THINK THEIR STRIKER WAS HAMPERED BY HIS STRAIT-JACKET
BUT FANCY MISS GRABWORTHY DOIN' A STREAK!
AN' I DIN'T KNOW OUR HEAD COULD FOAM AT THE MOUTH!
Maurice Dodd U287
ALL IN ALL A GAME TO REMEMBER WOULDN' YOU SAY?
WHO WON?
YEA

'ULLO SHAILOR (HIC)
ZOUNDS- 'TIS TATTY OLDBITT (THE SAILOR'S FRIEND)
DRUNK AGAIN I SEE
Maurice Dodd

REELY? CRIPESH-YOU ARE FORTUNATE

WHEN I'M DRUNK...
WHOOPSH
...I CAN'T SHEE A THING
CLANG
U288

OI-'OO CLOSED THE 'ATCH?
THE NAVY'S NEVER BEEN THE SAME SINCE THEY STOPPED THE GROG RATION
CRIPES YOU HAFTA DO EVERYTHIN' Y'SELF
OPEN THE 'ATCH SOMEBODY
U289

'OOS ARE THESE ROSHEBUD LIPS-SO CLOSHE TO MINE?
AH-THERE YOU ARE SHAILOR

GISHA KISH
ER...AH... MAY I ENQUIRE AS TO WHAT YOU'RE DOING IN A MANHOLE?

I THOUGHT I WAS IN A SHUBMARINE!
MAN'OLE?
Maurice Dodd

LISTEN, TATTY OLDBITT -YOU'RE NOT IN A SUBMARINE - YOU'RE IN A MANHOLE
IN WEST CRUNGE
U290
WESHT...?
Y'MEAN I'M NOT IN SCAPA?
SCAPA? WHY SHOULD YOU BE IN SCAPA?
WELL THEY WERE THE LASHT INSHTRUCTIONSH I RECEIVED
-THEY SHOVED A BOTTLE OF VODKA IN ME 'AND AN' SHOUTED 'SCAPA -SCAPA'
Maurice Dodd

I STRONGLY SUSPECT THAT THE PERSONS WHO THRUST THE VODKA AT YOU AND SHOUTED 'SCAPA' WERE EMPLOYING A COLLOQUIALISM
TO WIT- 'SCARPER'-MEANING KINDLY REMOVE YOUR PE
Maurice Dodd
NEVER MIND THE SMUTTY TALK 'ELP ME OUTA THIS 'OLE
OH VERY WELL
U291
OOPS -SORRY
YIPE
SLAM
LISHEN, MATEY, AN IMPASSIONED NIBBLE IS ONE THING - BUT YOU DON'T GO ROUN' BITIN' LADIES TAILSH!

LISTEN, MADAM OLDBITT- I DID NOT BITE YOUR TAIL
SHORRY DEARIE-MUSH BE ALL THE VODKA I'VE BEEN DRINKIN'
I DIN'T KNOW IT COULD GIVE YOU A PAIN IN THE TAIL
IN MY OPINION YOU'RE BADLY HUNG-OVER
I'LL THANK YOU TO KEEP YOUR PERSH'NAL REMARKSH TO YOURSHELF
AN' WOT'S MORE MOSH' BLOKES LIKE THE WAY I'M BUILT
Maurice Dodd
U292

WHY'VE YOU BEEN DRINKING QUANTITIES OF VODKA?
WELL-IT ALL SHTARTED AT THE CHAPLAIN'S TEA-PARTY
TEA-PARTY?
YESH
WE WASH 'AVIN' A RIGHT OLE KNEESH-UP
WELL-I WAS 'AVIN' A RIGHT OLE KNEESH-UP
THEN SHOME BRIGHT SHPARK SHUGGESTED A GAME OF PASH-THE-PARCEL
AN' THE NEX' THING-I WASH IN A PARCEL, BELTIN' ALONG ON A RUSSIAN TRAIN
U293
WHAT MAKES YOU THINK IT WAS A RUSSIAN TRAIN?
THE PARCEL WAS MARKED WITH A DIRTY-GREAT RED-STAR
CUNNIN' OBSERVATION, DEARIE
Maurice Dodd

DIDN'T YOU WONDER WHAT YOU WERE DOING-WRAPPED IN A PARCEL ON A RUSSIAN TRAIN?
WELL IT WASH OBVIOUSH WASH'N' IT?
U294
I'D BEEN SHECONDED FOR A **SHECRET MISSION**
WELL WHAT WAS THE OBJECTIVE?
WELL O'COURSE THEY DIDN'T TELL ME **THAT**
THA'S HOW I **KNOW** IT WASH A SHECRET (HIC) MISSION
Maurice Dodd

SO THERE YOU WERE-ON A SECRET MISSION IN A PARCEL ON BOARD A RUSSIAN TRAIN..
HOW DID YOU GET OFF THE TRAIN?
WELL THE NEX' THING I KNEW I WASH BEIN' UNWRAPPED BY A BUNCH OF RUSSIAN SHAILORS
U295
I WASH ON A **RUSSIAN WARSHIP** -ON THE VULGAR
-THE VOLGA? -HOW DID YOU KNOW IT WAS THE VOLGA?
-YOU'VE 'EARD OF THAT SHONG -THE VULGAR BOATMEN?
Maurice Dodd
ER... YES
WELL THEY DON'T COME ANY MORE VULGAR THAN **THAT** LITTLE LOT WERE (I'M HAPPY TO SHAY)

YOU WERE ON A RUSSIAN WARSHIP?
WHAT WAS IT CALLED?
THE VLADIVAR (HIC)
Maurice Dodd
SOUNDS RUSSIAN... IN FACT IT SOUNDS FAMILIAR
WE WAS DOCKED-AT WARRINGTON
U296
WARRINGTON? -BUT WARRINGTON'S IN LANCASHIRE
WOT?
D'YOU KNOW WOT THIS MEANS?
THE RUSSKIES HAVE SHTOLEN LANCASHIRE!

LISTEN. TATTY-THE 'VLADIVAR' WASN'T ON THE VOLGA
IT, AND YOU, WERE ON THE MANCHESTER SHIP CANAL
WOT? THEM CRAFTY RUSSKIES -GETTIN' THEIR SHIP ALL THE WAY UP THERE UNDETECTED
U297
I DIN'T THINK THEY 'AD IT IN 'EM
I MEAN- AS SHAILORS THEY SHEEMED USHELESH
Maurice Dodd
USELESS? -WHY?
THEY SHPENT ALL THEIR TIME MOONLIGHTIN'-DISHTILLIN' (HIC) VODKA

THEY WERE DISTILLING VODKA -ON A WARSHIP?
YESH- CRATES OF THE SHTUFF- VATS OF THE SHTUFF

THERE WASH SHO MUCH VODKA IT WASH SHPILLIN' OUTA ME EARSH
U298
Maurice Dodd

WHY DID YOU DRINK SO MUCH OF IT?
WELL I 'AD TO KEEP TOPPIN' UP-COSH IT WASH SHPILLIN' OUTA ME EARSH

WERE THESE RUSSIAN SAILORS SPEAKING RUSSIAN?
NO, THE CRAFTY LOT-THEY WEREN'T LETTIN' ON
AN' THEY WAS ALL WEARIN' TRIPE 'N' ONION ACCENTSH
U299
BUT I CAUGHT 'EM OUT -I SHOUTED 'DO SVEDANEYA' AN' THEY KNEW 'XAC'LY WOT IT MEANT
SO I KEP' SHOUTIN' IT
Maurice Dodd
AND WHAT, PRECISELY DOES IT MEAN?
WELL, ROUGHLY TRANSHLATED IT MEANSH *'EVERY TIME I SHOUT THIS WE HAFTA HAVE ANOTHER (HIC) DRINK'*

WELL, HOW DID YOU MANAGE TO LEAVE THE 'VLADIVAR'?
BY WAY OF A FAREWELL PARTY
MIND YOU IT SHTARTED OFF ASH JUSHT A PARTY-THE FAREWELL KINDA DEVELOPED
JUSHT COSH I MADE A SHPEECH
U300
Maurice Dodd
I GOT ASH FAR ASH 'IT GIVESH ME GREAT PLEASHURE...'
AN' THEY ALL RAN AWAY
THAT WASH WHEN THE CAPTAIN PUSHED A BOTTLE OF VODKA INTO ME 'AND AN' SHOUTED 'SCAPA-SCAPA'
-AND YOU THOUGHT HE MEANT SCAPA-FLOW
ERE-'OO YOU CALLIN' FLO? MY NAME AIN'T FLO
YOUR MIND'S GOIN' SHAILOR, YOU'D BETTER LAY OFF THE (HIC) GROG

ER.... AH.... TATTY-I'VE BEEN WONDERING WHETHER TO TELL YOU THIS
BUT YOU HAVEN'T BEEN ON A RUSSIAN WARSHIP-YOU'VE BEEN IN A DISTILLERY
DISHTILLERY?
Maurice Dodd
D'YOU THINK I'M GA-GA?
D'YOU THINK I DON'T KNOW THE DIFFERENCE BETWEEN A BATTLESHIP AN' A BOOZE-BOILER?
U301
WELL, THANK YOU SHAILOR-AN' GOODYBYE
TAXI!

SEE HERE, TATTY OLDBITT, YOU'RE MAKING A BIG MISTAKE
IT'S YOU WHO'VE MADE THE MISHTAKE, SHAILOR, AN' IT'S NO USHE YOU 'ANGIN' ROUN'
I'M TAKIN' THISH CAB TO (HIC) POMPEY-RIGHT AWAY
U302
RIGHT, DRIVER, TAKE ME TO NAVAL INTELLIGENCE, PORTSMOUTH
YOU'LL FIND THEM AT THE 'MIGHTY FINE', COMMERCIAL ROAD
I'M GOIN' TO BE DE-BRIEFED (WIV ANY LUCK) BY SOME 'IGH RANKIN' SHTOKERSH
WELL SHTEP ON IT, MY MAN, I 'AVEN'T GOT TILL CHRISHMASH
'ROLL ME O-VER IN THE CLO-VER'

YOO-HOO, MARLON-ARE YOU THINKIN' ABOUT CHRIS'MAS PREZZIES?
WELL, NO, MAISIE -I'M THINKIN' ABOUT A SAUSAGE SARNIE
WELL D'YOU THINK YOU COULD START THINKIN' ABOUT CHRIS'MAS PREZZIES?
FOR A CERTAIN (TEE-HEE) PARTY
OH-I THINK I COULD
WHAT I'D DO IS KEEP SAYIN' CHRIS'MAS PREZZIES TO MYSELF AN' THEN SOONER OR LATER...
YOU'RE BEIN' VERY SHIFTY
NO I'M NOT -I'VE 'ARDLY MOVED A MUSCLE
U303
WELL ALL RIGHT-IF IT'S THAT IMPORTANT I'LL MAKE A LIST OF WOT I'D LIKE AN' GIVE IT TO YOU TOMORROW
Maurice Dodd

I'M ON MY WAY TO GIVE SEASONAL GREETINGS TO COUSIN WORSOFF
THE ONE WHO'S ALWAYS THAN YOURSELF?
THE VERY SAME
THE ONE WHO LIVES DOWN THE DRAIN HOLE -SEARCHIN' FOR THE MEANIN' OF LIFE?
AN' WHO'S GOT THE WORL'S LARGES' COLLECTION OF INTERESTINLY WRINKLED OLE ORANGE PEEL?
YOU REMEMBER HIM WELL
H'LO COUSIN WORSOFF -MERRY CHRISTMAS
YEA- ME TOO
THRUPPP
WORSOFF NEVER COULD JOIN IN THE SPIRIT OF THINGS
Maurice Dodd
U304

CHRIS'MAS IS COMIN', THE GEESE ARE GETTIN' FAT, PLEASE PUT A PENNY IN THE OLE MAN'S HAT
IF YOU HAVEN'T GOT A PENNY A HA'PENNY WILL DO
IF YOU HAVEN'T GOT A HA'PENNY WELL GOD BLESS YOU
i find that doggerel lacking both cohesion and credibility
since i fail to see how overweight geese fit into the narrative
and i'm sure the average senior citizen would strenuously resist coinage being thrust under his head gear
and since the ha'penny is no longer viable currency god would need to shower blessings in the manner of confetti
so i seriously suggest you up-date your repertoire
Maurice Dodd
U305

WHAT WITH ALL THE FUN AN' EXCITEMENT-AN' THE FOOD, CRUMBS-THE FOOD (HAVE A CHOC'LATE CIGAR)
TA
U306
WELL I'M REALLY LOOKIN' FORWARD TO TOMORROW -AREN'T YOU?
OH YES-A DAY DEVOTED TO MADCAP MIRTH AN' MERRIMENT
CULMINATIN' WITH TOASTIN' THE TOES AT THE OLE YULE LOG WHEN FILLED TO OVER FLOWIN' AN' BURSTIN' AT THE SEAMS
MINE YOU-IT COULD PROVE DIFFICULT SQUEEZIN' ALL THAT OUT 'VE TWO BALLOONS, HALF A POUND OF BANGERS AN' A COUPLE OF OVAL MARIES
BUT WE'LL TRY-WE'LL TRY
Maurice Dodd

WE OUGHT TO GO FOR A BIG LONG WALK, BOOT

WALK OFF THE EFFECTS OF THE CHRIS'MAS DINNER
Maurice Dodd
U307

WELL-CONSIDERING THE SIZE OF **OUR** CHRISTMAS DINNER...
-THAT'S FAR ENOUGH

...AN' I GOT A DOLLIE AN'A DOLLIE'S PRAM AN' A DOLLIE'S COT AN' A NEW TRANNIE AN' A BIG BIG BOX OF CHOCS
U308

AN' I'M SORRY IF I'VE MADE YOU JEALOUS
OH DON'T WORRY-YOU HAVEN'T

WOT? NOT AT ALL?
NOT IN THE TEENIEST BIT

YOU TAKE ALL THE FUN OUTA CHRIS'MAS
MauriceDodd

AN' DID SANTA DROP IN ON YOU WELLIN'TON?
I B'LIEVE HE DID, MAISIE -I B'LIEVE HE DID
U309

AN' DID HE LEAVE YOU LOTS 'N' LOTS OF LOVELY PREZZIES?
WELL-NOT EXAC'LY

-HE ONLY CALLED IN TO USE THE LOO
MauriceDodd

U310

PANT-PANT-
GASP-PANT

GASP-PANT-
CHOKE-PANT

GASP-
CHOKE-WHEEZE
-PANT
ALL
RIGHT-
ALL
RIGHT
-I SPEND
MORE TIME FILLIN'
YOUR WATER-
BOWL...
Maurice Dodd

JUS' THINK,
BOOT-HERE WE
ARE, IN A BRAN'
NEW YEAR
BOOT
WHAT WILL
IT BE LIKE-WHAT
DOES IT HAVE IN
STORE?
BOOT
V1
WILL IT BE A
YEAR FULL OF HOPE
-A YEAR FULL OF
PROMISE?
IF IT
DOESN'T START OFF
WITH A BOWL-FULL
OF SCOFF I'M NEVER
GOING TO
MAKE IT!
Maurice Dodd

WELL ONCE AGAIN WE'VE COME AWAY WITHOUT A ROSETTE OR AN ANYTHIN'
I DON'T KNOW WHAT IT IS-IT'S NOT THAT YOU'RE NOT BRIGHT ENOUGH
-YOU JUS' DON'T SEEM TO BE ABLE TO SHINE IN THE RING
I DON'T THINK I'LL BOTHER TO PUT YOU IN FOR ANYMORE TRIALS
AMEN TO THAT SAY I -AMEN TO THAT
THOSE DAMN HORSE-SHOWS ARE KILLING ME!
V2

-NOT MUCH IN THE POST TODAY, BOOT
AMERICAN EXPRESS HAVE OFFERED ME A GOLD CARD WITH FACILITIES FOR UNLIMITED SPENDIN' AN'A £7,500 OVERDRAFT
A SIMILAR GENEROUS OFFER HAS COME FROM DINERS CLUB
READERS DIGEST HAVE CHOSEN MY NAME FROM THOUSANDS AS THE LIKELY WINNER OF A FORTUNE
SOMEBODY ELSE WANTS ME TO TEST DRIVE A MERCEDES AN' WIN A VILLA IN SPAIN
V3
D'YOU THINK, MAYBE, THEY'VE GOT THE WRONG BLOKE?
LICK LICK

NOW WE'RE INTO THE NEW YEAR, BOOT, WE SHOULD BE HAVIN' A REVIEW
DRONE DRONE, DRONE -TAKIN' STOCK- MAKIN' AN INVENTORY...
OH VERY WELL
...ONE DISH, ONE CHEWED-UP BALL, ONE SUPERANNUATED BONE
BOOT
DRONE, DRONE RHUBARB, DRONE -TAKE A GOOD LOOK ROUN' AN' SEE WHERE WE'RE AT
OH I KNOW WHERE WE ARE ALL RIGHT
BUT YOU WON'T FIND 'PENURY' ON THE MAP
DRONE DRONE, DRONE DRONE ZZ ZZZZZZZ ZZZ
Maurice Dodd
V4

WE SHOULD BE LOOKIN' TO THE FUTURE, BOOT
WE SHOULD TRY TO SEE WHAT LIES AHEAD
SCRATCH SCRATCH SCRATCH
I MEAN. WHAT, WHEREFORE AN' WITHER?
WHERE ARE WE GOIN'-THAT'S WHAT I WANT TO KNOW
-APART FROM 'WALKIES' THAT IS
Maurice Dodd
V5

YOU WERE RIGHT, BOOT- A WALK IN THE WILD IS JUS' WHAT WE NEEDED
TO STEP FROM OUR MAD RUSHIN' WORL' AN' BREATH IN THE ANCIENT ALCHEMY OF MOTHER NATURE
TO MARVEL AT THE GOSSAMER SKELETON OF A DEAD LEAF
AN' CHANCE UPON A SECRET TROVE OF OLE GAS-PIPES
I S'POSE SOME SHY CREATURE OF THE WILD WINTER'S WARMLY IN THIS SNUG HOLLOW
V6
OW, YEA LANGUISHIN' IDLY ON A MESS OF WET LEAVES AN' COVERED IN FLEAS - IT'S THE ONLY WAY TO WINTER YOU GREAT LOLLOPIN' BERK!
Maurice Dodd

S'MARVELLOUS ISN' IT, BOOT?
THE BRITTLE SKY MARBLED BY STREAMIN' CLOUDS
THE SWAGGERIN' ROOKS AN' CHIRPY SPARROWS
AN' THERE'S THE MERRY ROBIN
SYMBOL OF CHEER MIDST WINTER'S CIRCLIN' GLOOM
Maurice Dodd
OW YOU DO 'AVE A WAY WITH WORDS IF I MAY (OOGH AAGH, CRIPES) SAY SO (GASP) SQUIRE
V7

IT'S AMAZIN' HOW NATURE STRUGGLES ON-DEFYIN' WINTER'S ICY GRIP
PRIMROSES AN' CROCUSESSES REVEAL THEIR DELICATE CHARMS
SOMEWHERE OR THE OTHER
AN' SOON THE GOLDEN DAFFODILS WILL BE NODDIN' THEIR WELSH BONCES IN THE BREEZE
V8
OH-A GARDEN IS A LOVESOME THING GOD WOT!
COR-I COULDN' HALF DO WITH A SAUSAGE SARNIE
THERE'S NOTHING LIKE A BIT OF GOD-WOTTERY FOR WORKING UP AN APPETITE

IT'S TIME WE HEADED HOME, BOOT-IT'S GETTIN' A BIT COLD
V9
WE'VE BEEN OUT A WHOLE HALF-HOUR
HERE-THAT CROW LOOKS A BIT FIERCE
CRUMBS -MY EARS ARE FREEZIN'
MY NOSE IS BEGINNIN' TO DRIP
NATURE'S NOT EVERYTHIN' IT'S CRACKED UP TO BE
MY WELLIES HAVE SPRUNG A LEAK
YEUK-I'VE JUS' TRODDEN IN SOMETHIN' NASTY
I DON'T THINK I'M CUT-OUT FOR THIS NATURE RAMBLIN' LARK
YOU DO SURPRISE ME
-YOU'VE DONE MORE RAMBLING IN THE LAST HALF-HOUR THAN I'VE HEARD IN MANY A DAY

CRUMBS, BOOT-A BIT OF A WIND'S SPRUNG UP
AN' IT'S GETTIN' STRONGER
S'MORE LIKE A GALE
FORCE 500 AT LEAST I'D SAY
V10
COR WHOOSH- IT'S BRACIN' ISN'T IT?
BRACING? BY THE LORD HARRY I SHOULD SAY IT IS

I'M GOING TO WALK BACKWARDS THE REST OF THE WAY

CRUMBS, BOOT, WHAT A WIND!
I'VE NEVER KNOWN SUCH A....
BOOT?
BOOT?
V11

WILL YOU STOP MESSIN' ABOUT!

JUMP, BOOT, JUMP
COME ON–YOU'LL COME TO NO HARM
V12

WHAT'S IT LIKE IN THERE?

CRUMBS, BOOT, YOU REALLY ARE STUCK FAST!
I DON'T THINK ANY AMOUNT OF PULLIN'..
V13

–WAIT– I'VE GOT A NIDEA
MAYBE INSTEAD OF PULLIN'...

RIGHT IF YOU C'N SQUEEZE UP PAST THAT NARROW BIT –Y'GOT IT MADE

LOOK ON THE BRIGHT SIDE, BOOT-THERE'S ALWAYS A BRIGHT SIDE

I MEAN- THE WIND IS ACTUALLY HELPIN' US NOW

Y'SEE- THERE'S ALWAYS A SILVER LI~
NING!
V14

LOOK AT IT THIS WAY
WE'RE IN ABSOLUTELY NO DANGER OF GATHERIN' MOSS
Maurice Dodd
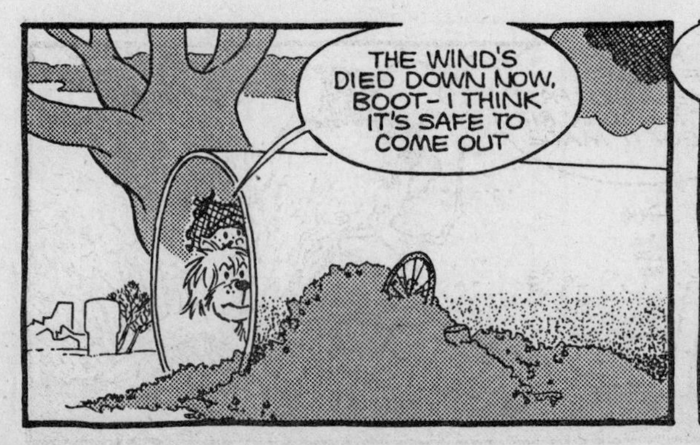
THE WIND'S DIED DOWN NOW, BOOT- I THINK IT'S SAFE TO COME OUT

THAT WIND WAS AWFUL WASN' IT?
I COULDN' THINK OF ANYTHIN' WORSE THAN THAT WIND
Maurice Dodd
V15

IF HE SAYS "ON SECON' THOUGHTS" I'LL KILL HIM

CRUMBS, BOOT, WHAT A DAY
FIRST GALE FORCE WINDS AN' NOW DRIVIN' RAIN

STILL-WE'RE HOME 'N' DRY NOW, SAFE FROM THE ELEMENTS

I DON'T THINK BROKEN GUTTERIN' COUNTS AS ELEMENTS...
Maurice Dodd
V16

CRUMBS, BOOT-I'M SATURATED

EVERY STITCH OF CLOTHING IS SOAKED
V17

COR-THAT'S BETTER

THERE IS NO NEED TO LOSE YOUR TEMPER
Maurice Dodd

IT WAS ALMOS' WORTH GETTIN' COLD AN' WET TO DRY OFF IN FRONT OF A GOOD FIRE, BOOT
MINE YOU IT'S NOT GOIN' TO BE A GOOD FIRE FOR MUCH LONGER UNLESS SOMEBODY GOES OUT FOR A BUCKET OF COAL
I KNOW IT'S COLD AN' WET AN' SPOOKY OUT THERE BUT DO I HEAR ANY VOLUNTEERS?
WELL LET'S HOPE THAT LAST LUMP HOLDS OUT LONG ENOUGH FOR US TO HAVE AN EARLY NIGHT
V18
Maurice Dodd

WHAT DID YOU DO YESTERDAY, WELLIN'TON?
OLE BOOT 'N' ME WENT FOR A LONG WALK
I DUNNO HOW YOU C'N STAN' THE EXCITEMENT–IS THAT ALL YOU DID?
YEA, WELL–THE YACHT'S IN DRY-DOCK, THE ROLLS IS IN FOR SERVICIN' AN' THE DECORATORS ARE IN AT THE COUNTRY MANSION
V19
POO–I S'POSE YOU THINK THAT'S VERY FUNNY
WELL, NOT REALLY–BUT YOU SEE...
THE JOKE BOOK'S IN FOR REBINDIN'
Maurice Dodd

WELL THIS IS AS FAR AS YOU GO, BABY GRUMPLIN' - I'LL SEE YOU TONIGHT
MINE YOU- PRETTY SOON NOW YOU'LL BE STARTIN' SCHOOL YOURSELF
oh, well- look on the bright side
before then they might've found a way of arresting growth
V20
MauriceDodd

IT'S ALL BAD NEWS AGAIN THIS MORNIN', BOOT
I SOMETIMES WONDER IF THERE'S ANY HOPE FOR MANKIND
WELL, AS YOU KNOW -I DO NOT PATRONISE THE POPULAR PRESS
YET I CONSTANTLY ENTERTAIN THOUGHTS OF A SIMILAR NATURE
V21
MauriceDodd

ER..MARLON?
D'YOU THINK I'M BEAUTIFUL?
TO BE HONES'-NO, MAISIE
OH? WELL JUS' WHO DO YOU THINK IS BEAUTIFUL?
WELL.... THERE'S SAMANTHA FOX, SELINA SCOTT, JOANNA LUMLEY...
(SNIFF) I BET NONE OF THEM'VE GOT A BAG OF CHOC'LATE CREAMS TO SHARE OUT AT PLAYTIME
ATTRACTIVE, MAISIE - THAT'S WHAT YOU SHOULD'VE ASKED. DO I THINK YOU'RE ATTRACTIVE?
V22
Maurice Dodd

WHO'S BEEN AT MY SWEETIE TIN?
WHO PINCHED A SWEETIE FROM MY ROOM?
WELL?
i cannot tell a lie
well-only to save a friend
i might definitely tell a lie to divert suspicion from a dear old friend
so it wasn't 'gladly' mi cross-eyed bear
V23
Maurice Dodd

ARE YOU GOIN' TO HAVE A GAME WITH THE FORT, MARLON?
NO THANKS, WELLIN'TON- I'M STUDYIN' THIS BOOK ON HOW TO BE A BRAIN SURGEON
V24
....LESSON ONE... LO-CA-TIN' THE BRAIN...
SEE DI-A-GRAM 'A'..
CRUMBS- IT'S JUST AS WELL I SAW THIS BEFORE GOIN' ON TO THE 'PRACTICAL'
I ALWAYS THOUGHT THE BRAIN WAS SOMEWHERE NEAR THE TOP
YOU'RE HOLDIN' THE DIAGRAM UPSIDE-DOWN

I DUNNO WHAT MAKES YOU THINK YOU COULD BE A BRAIN SURGEON ANYWAY
'COS I'M GOOD WIV ME 'ANDS- THAS WHY
V25
I MEAN- LOOK AT THAT RABBIT-'UTCH I MADE LAS' WEEK
OH, YES - A MAGNIFRICENT CONSTRUCTION
EVEN IF YOU COULDN' GET ANY RABBITS INTO IT
'COS YOU FORGOT TO PUT IN ANY DOORS
POO- A PETTY DETAIL
ANYWAY- BRAINS DON' 'AVE DOORS

I THOUGHT YOU'D GIVEN UP THE MAD DREAM OF BEIN' A BRAIN - SURGEON
IN FAVOUR OF BEIN' A SEWER-OPERATIVE
OW, YEA A BLOKE-WOT-GOES-DOWN-SEWERS-IN-BIG-RUBBER-BOOTS...

IF ONLY IT COULD BE-BUT THAT CALLS FOR A GREAT DEAL OF SKILL AN' PATIENCE
Maurice Dodd

- THEM BOOTS IS VERY TRICKY TO PULL ON
V26

THERE'S ANOTHER SNAG TO BEIN' A BLOKE-WOT-GOES-DOWN-SEWERS-IN-BIG-RUBBER-BOOTS
Maurice Dodd

-THERE'S ALL THE GEAR YOU HAFTA HAVE
BOOTS, OVERALLS, THINGS ON LONG POLES-IT COULD COST A FORTUNE
DON'T YOU THINK A BRAIN-SURGEON MIGHT NEED A FEW ITEMS OF EQUIPMENT?
OW YEA, BUT THEY'RE HALFWAY THERE TO START....
-'COS THE CUSTOMERS HAFTA SUPPLY THEIR OWN BRAINS!
V27

WELL I STILL THINK YOU SHOULD GO FOR BEIN' A SEWER-OPERATIVE RATHER THAN A BRAIN-SURGEON
THAT SHOWS LIMITED THINKIN'-I'M GOIN' TO DO BOTH
I'M GOIN' T'BE A BLOKE-WOT-GOES-DOWN-SEWERS-IN-BIG-RUBBER-BOOTS-FULL-TIME
AN' DO A BIT OF PART-TIME BRAIN-SURGERY AT HOME
AT HOME?
WHERE'VE YOU GOT ROOM FOR AN OPERATIN' THEATRE AN' BEDS FOR PATIENTS TO RECOVER AN' EVERYTHIN'
I'M CUTTIN' OUT LOOKIN' AFTER PATIENTS AN' ALL THAT OLE STUFF
I'M ONLY TAKIN' THEIR 'EADS
V28

D' YOU REALLY THINK BRAIN SURGEONS CUT OFF PEOPLE'S HEADS?
WELL-STAN'S TO REASON DUNNIT?
-YOU CUT OFF THE 'EAD AN' SHAKE THE BRAINS DOWN THROUGH THE 'OLE IN THE NECK AN'
YOU GET AT PEOPLE'S BRAINS BY SAWIN' THROUGH THE TOPS OF THEIR HEADS
SAWIN' THROUGH THE? ....(GULP)
-IT'S A GOOD JOB YOU'RE NOT GOIN' TO BE A BRAIN SURGEON
V29

YOU'N YOUR STUPID IDEAS ABOUT BRAIN SURGERY - YOU'LL DRIVE ME BONKERS
IF Y'ASK ME Y'R ALREADY BONKERS
WHAT WITH WANTIN' TO SAW THE TOPS OFF PEOPLE'S 'EADS AN'..
WELLIN'TON- WHAT'RE YOU DOIN' TO MY MARLON?
HE'S GOIN' THROUGH HIS WANTIN' TO BE A BRAIN SURGEON PHASE AGAIN-IT'S DRIVIN' ME UP THE WALL
WELL HE'S TRYIN TO MAKE SOMETHIN' OF HIMSELF- HE DESERVES ENCOURAGEMENT
YEA RIGHT, MAISIE, RIGHT
-LEND US Y'R 'EAD
V30

H'LO, MARLON
LOOK-I'M SORRY I WENT ON ABOUT YOU WANTIN'T'BE A BRAIN SURGEON
V31
WHAT'RE YOU DOIN'?
I'M RE-WRITIN' THE BRAIN SURGERY WORKSHOP MANUAL -I'VE THOUGHT UP A BRILLIANT NEW METHOD
....SECTION TWO-ESSENTIAL EQUIPMENT...
ER... WELLIN'TON?
HOW D'YOU SPELL BICYCLE-PUMP?

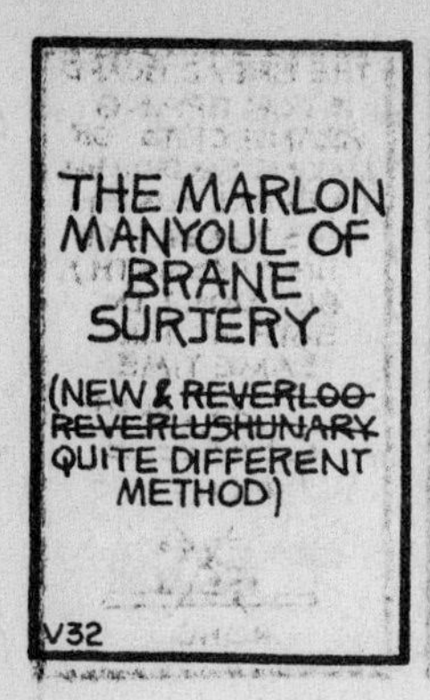
THE MARLON MANYOUL OF BRANE SURJERY
(NEW & ~~REVERLOO REVERLUSHUNARY~~ QUITE DIFFERENT METHOD)
V32

OUT GO THE OLD CRUDE METHOD & ~~EKWIPM~~ TOOLS
PUFF PUFF
(NO MORE TIRIN' SAWIN')

OUT GO THE OLD STODJY THEATER COSTUMES

IN COMES THE NEW (KEEP IT LIGHTEARTED) GEAR
JOKE BOOK

BRANE SURJERY CAN BE FUN!
HA HA HA HA
IS EVERYBODY 'APPY?
NOT ARF GUGNOR *
← BRANE
*SEE SPECIAL SECTION ON VENTRILOKWISM

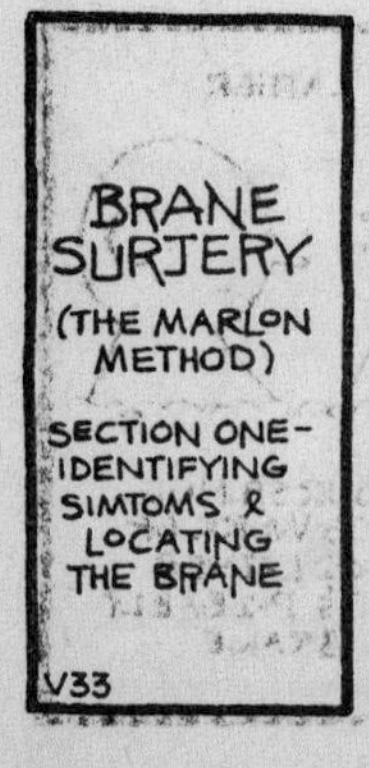
BRANE SURJERY
(THE MARLON METHOD)
SECTION ONE - IDENTIFYING SIMTOMS & LOCATING THE BRANE
V33

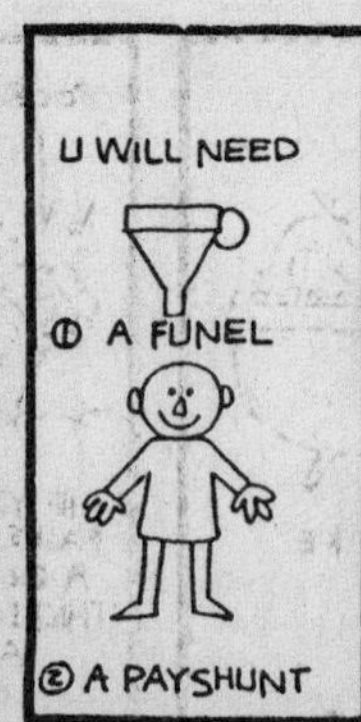
U WILL NEED
① A FUNEL
② A PAYSHUNT

A PAYSHUNT NEEDING BRANE SURJERY WILL TEND TO-
Ⓐ BUMP INTO THINGS
Ⓑ KEEP FALLING OVER

MI BRANE 'URTS
Ⓒ COMPLANE

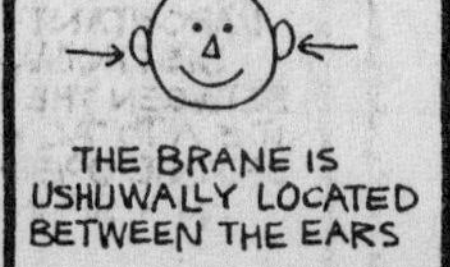
THE BRANE IS USHUWALLY LOCATED BETWEEN THE EARS

OI!
TO VERIFY - PLAICE PAYSHUNT ON CHAIR & FUNEL IN EAR (THE PAYSHUNTS EAR) THEN SHOUT INTO FUNEL
Y
IF PASHUNT JUMPS THEN THE BRANE IS IN & YOU MAY PROSEED TO THE NEXT STAGE

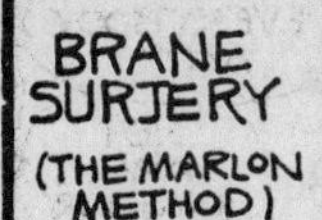
BRANE SURJERY
(THE MARLON METHOD)
SECTION TWO - OPERATING TOOLS & PROSEEDURE
V34

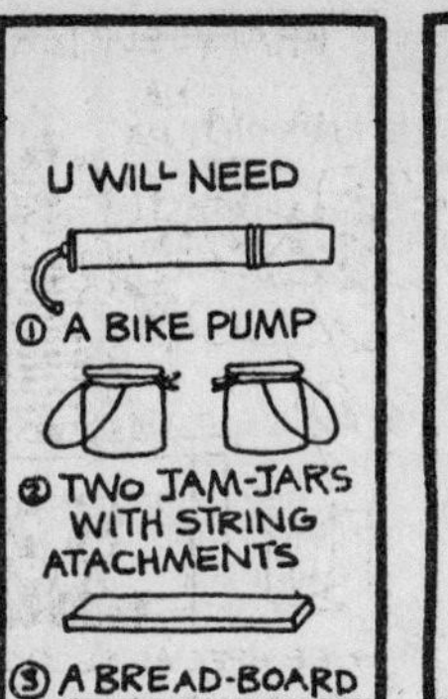

U WILL NEED
① A BIKE PUMP
② TWO JAM-JARS WITH STRING ATACHMENTS
③ A BREAD-BOARD

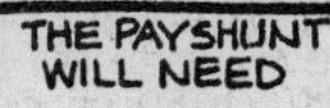

THE PAYSHUNT WILL NEED
A RELIABLE FRIEND (TO SEE HIM HOME COS YOU DON'T WANT HIM HANGING ABOUT WILE YOUR MENDING HIS BRANE)

PROSEEDURE
① HANG JAR ON PAYSHUNT'S EAR
② PLAICE PUMP NOSSEL IN PAYSHUNT'S EAR
③ PULL HANDEL - THUS EGGSTRACTING BRANE

A WISE PRECAUSHUN!
PLAICE OTHER JAR ON PAYSHUNT'S OTHER EAR - IN CASE YOU PUSH HANDEL
Maurice Dodd

THE BREAD BOARD IS FOR TIPPING BRANE ONTO OR MAKING SANDWICHES (A BRANE SURJEN HAS TO KEEP UP HIS STRENKTH) BUT DON'T DO BOTH AT THE SAME TIME
BRANE
RIGHT
RONG

BRANE SURJERY
(THE MARLON METHOD)
SECTION THREE IDENTIFYING THE BRANE
V35

WUNCE YOU HAVE GOT YOUR BRANE TAKE A GOOD LOOK AT IT
YOU WILL FIND IT LOOKS VERY MUCH LIKE A SPUNGE

A COMPARISON IS USEFUL
BRANE
SPUNGE
IT IS VERY IMPORTANT TO DISTINGWISH BETWEEN THE TWO - IT IS A TOTAL WAIST OF TIME OPERATING ON A SPUNGE

IF IN DOUBT - TAKE A BATH
Maurice Dodd

POOR LATHER
IF YOUR SPUNGE FAILS TO WORK UP A GOOD LATHER THEN IT'S PROBABLY A BRANE

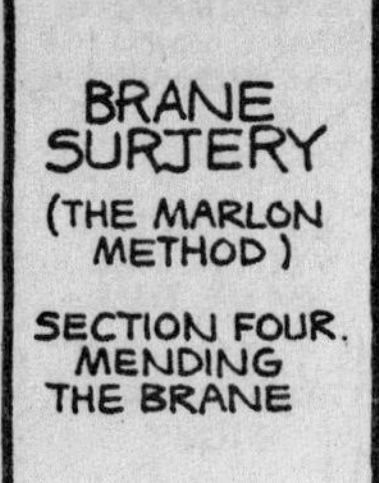
BRANE SURJERY
(THE MARLON METHOD)
SECTION FOUR. MENDING THE BRANE
V36

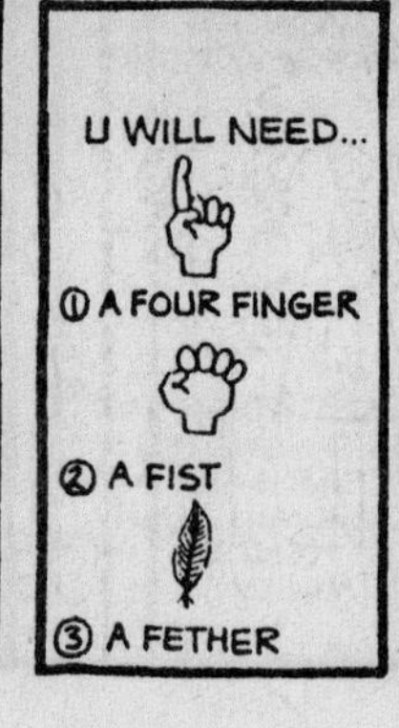
U WILL NEED...
① A FOUR FINGER
② A FIST
③ A FETHER

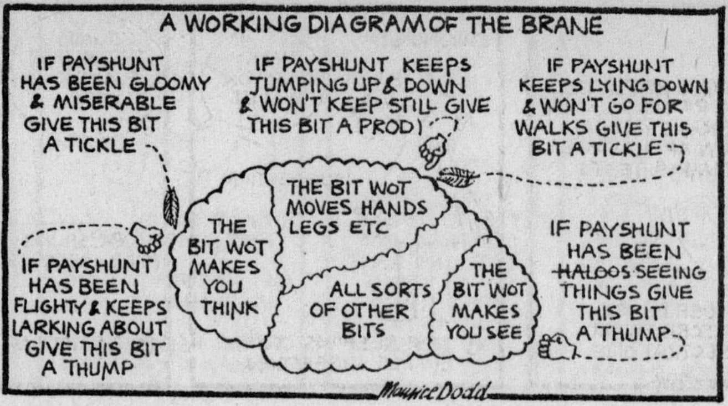
A WORKING DIAGRAM OF THE BRANE
IF PAYSHUNT HAS BEEN GLOOMY & MISERABLE GIVE THIS BIT A TICKLE
IF PAYSHUNT KEEPS JUMPING UP & DOWN & WON'T KEEP STILL GIVE THIS BIT A PROD
IF PAYSHUNT KEEPS LYING DOWN & WON'T GO FOR WALKS GIVE THIS BIT A TICKLE
THE BIT WOT MOVES HANDS LEGS ETC
THE BIT WOT MAKES YOU THINK
ALL SORTS OF OTHER BITS
THE BIT WOT MAKES YOU SEE
IF PAYSHUNT HAS BEEN FLIGHTY & KEEPS LARKING ABOUT GIVE THIS BIT A THUMP
IF PAYSHUNT HAS BEEN ~~HALOOS~~ SEEING THINGS GIVE THIS BIT A THUMP
Maurice Dodd

FOR A REALLY PROFESHONAL FINISH-GIVE BRANE A GOOD DUSTING & A BIT OF A LICK & POLISH
A BRANE IN SHOWROOM CONDITION
YOU ARE NOW READY TO REPLACE THE BRANE

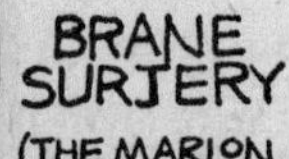
BRANE SURJERY
(THE MARLON METHOD)
SECTION FIVE REPLACING THE BRANE
V37

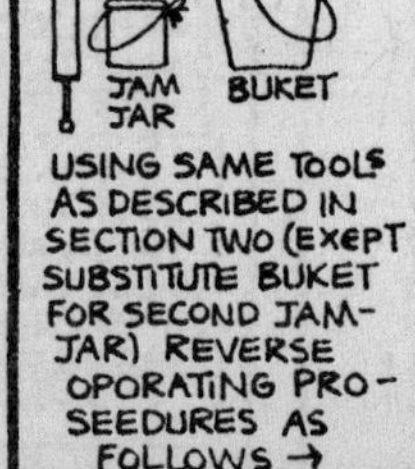
BIKE PUMP
JAM JAR
BUKET
USING SAME TOOLS AS DESCRIBED IN SECTION TWO (EXEPT SUBSTITUTE BUKET FOR SECOND JAM-JAR) REVERSE OPORATING PRO-SEEDURES AS FOLLOWS →

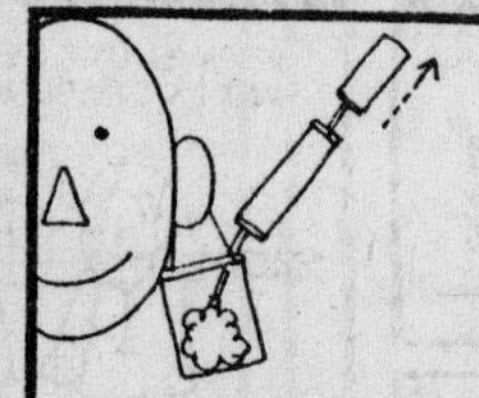
① PLACE BRANE IN JAM-JAR AND HANG ON PAY-SHUNTS EAR
② ATACHE BRANE TO PUMP NOSSLE USING SUCTION CAUSED BY PULLING HANDEL

③ PLACE BRANE AGAINST PAYSHUNTS EAR
④ PUSH HANDEL ~~VIGER- VIGORES - VIGOURSLY~~ VERY HARD
Maurice Dodd

IMPORTANT
OOPS!
FIRST HANG BUKET ON OTHER EAR IN CASE YOU PUSH TOO HARD
* IF THIS SHOULD HAPEN DON'T BE DISCURATED - PRACTISE MAKS PERFECT YOU KNOW!

BRANE SURJERY

(THE MARLON METHOD)

SECTION SIX TESTING THE RE-CONDISHOND BRANE

V38

HAVING RE-PLAICED THE RE-CONDISHOND BRANE YOU CAN NOW APPLY SOME SIMPLE TESTS

USE FUNEL DESCRIBED IN SECTION ONE

Maurice Dodd

Ⓐ TEST RESPONS TO SIMPLE SUGGESTION

Ⓑ TEST LOCOMOTIVE ABILITY

Ⓒ JUST ASK

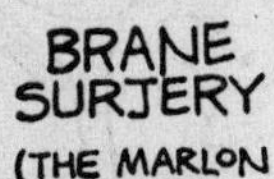

BRANE SURJERY

(THE MARLON METHOD)

SECTION SEVEN THE TEST-RUN

V39

HAVING RE-PLAICED & TESTED THE RE-CONDISHUND BRANE THE PAYSHUNT CAN NOW TAKE IT FOR A TEST-RUN

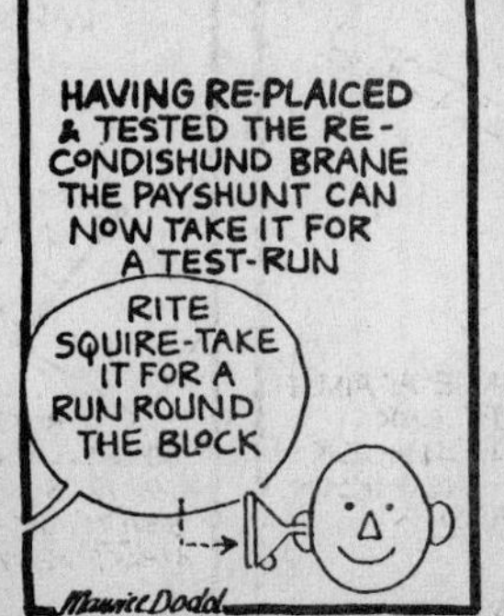

Maurice Dodd

STOP!

REMOVE FUNEL FIRST

IF PAYSHUNT RETURNS WITH A COMPLAYNT...

REFER HIM/HER TO THE COMPLAYNTS DEPT. (I THINK THERES WON AT HARRODS)

IF PAYSHUNT DOESN'T RETURN THE OPERASHUN HAS BEEN -

Ⓐ A ROARING SUCKSESS

Ⓑ A RIGHT BOG-UP

IN EITHER CASE YORE NOT LIKELY TO SEE HIM/HER AGANE SO YORE LARFING

A FINAL WARNING

NEVER GIVE A GARUNTEE. PAYSHUNT MAY CAUSE UNDUE WEAR ON BRANE BY EXESIFF THINKING & EGGSPECT YOU TO REPAIR IT AGANE F.O.C.!

WOT DID Y'THINK OF MY MANUAL ON BRAIN SURGERY, WELLIN'TON?
ER.. WELL... AH... I HARDLY KNOW HOW TO DESCRIBE IT, MARLON
HOW ABOUT MAGIC, KNOCKOUT, BRILLIANT, SUPER?
I WAS THINKING MORE IN TERMS OF ABYSMAL, INFANTILE, ASININE, DERANGED
V40
Maurice Dodd
OH YEA,?
REALLY?
-I DIN'T THINK IT WAS THAT GOOD!

ER... MAR-LON
YOU KNOW YOUR PLANS FOR BEIN' A BRAIN-SURGEON?
YEA, MAISIE
I DUNNO HOW TO PUT THIS
- BUT KISSY-FACE WOULD LOOK SO MUCH MORE HANSOME IN BIG RUBBER BOOTS
-BEIN' A BLOKE WHAT GOES DOWN SEWERS
THAT OLE SOFT SOAP DON'T FOOL ME
I KNOW WOT YOU'RE GETTIN' AT
V41
YOU'N YOUR DRIVIN' AMBITION
FOREVER PUSHIN' A BLOKE BEYOND 'IS CAPABILITIES
Maurice Dodd

WHAT FOUL WEATHER, BOOT
I HATE THIS ROTTEN WEATHER
V42
STILL-THEY SAY WE BRITISH DO NOTHIN' BUT MOAN AT THE WEATHER
HEY-THERE'S A THOUGHT THERE
S'POSE WE DIDN'T MOAN AT THE WEATHER -S'POSE WE WERE KIND TO IT?
MAYBE IT WOULD BE KIND TO US!
HEY THERE WEATHER-NICE WEATHER-KIND WEATHER-'OOS BEEN A GOOD WEATHER DEN?
I DO NOT WANT TO LIE DOWN IN A DARKENED ROOM
Maurice Dodd

-WELL IT'S WORTH A TRY
I'M GOIN' OUT THERE AN' TALK TO THE WEATHER-BE NICE TO THE WEATHER
V43
IF WE'RE NICE TO THE WEATHER-MAYBE THE WEATHER WILL BE NICE TO US
Maurice Dodd
-WELL -YOU NEVER KNOW
THIS WORL'S FULL OF STRANGE THINGS!
THAT HARDLY COMES AS NEWS TO ME

RIGHT BOOT, WE'LL GIVE IT A TRY
– IF WE'RE NICE TO THE WEATHER – MAYBE THE WEATHER WILL BE NICE TO US
HI THERE WEATHER, NICE WEATHER, THERE'S A GOOD WEATHER
OH COME ON, IS THAT THE BEST YOU CAN DO?
KABOOM
Maurice Dodd
V44

APPARENTLY IT WAS

ALL THIS WEATHER JUS' 'COS I MADE A CHANCE REMARK
OH I'M FED UP WITH THIS
WELL SEE IF I CARE. GO AHEAD - DO YOUR WORST

'ULLO, WELLIN'TON
GASP
GASP
Maurice Dodd
V45

-FUNNY WEATHER WE'RE 'AVIN'

-'ERE-IT'S SNOWIN'
MY WORD, MARLON-I THINK YOU'RE ONTO IT

GASP
GASP
AN' NOW IT'S HEATWAVIN' (GASP)
V46

AN' NOW IT'S RAININ'

IF YOU ASK ME THERE'S SOMETHIN' FUNNY GOIN' ON
Maurice Dodd

WOT'S GOIN' ON-THAT'S WOT I WANT TO KNOW-WOT IS GOIN' ON?

GASP
GASP
GASP
V47

Maurice Dodd

-I TAKE IT YOU'RE FAMILIAR WITH THE EXPRESSION *UNDER THE WEATHER*?

WADDAYA MEAN-HE'S GOT HIS OWN WEATHER?
YOU'LL SEE, HERE HE COMES NOW
V48
'LO, WELLIN'TON
OH- I SEE..
OUR WEATHER IS'N' GOOD ENOUGH FOR YOU A?
Maurice Dodd

LOOK, BOOT- JUS' 'COS I'VE UPSET THE WEATHER- THERE'S NO NEED FOR YOU TO SUFFER TOO
KEEP YOUR DISTANCE FROM ME (SIGH) I KNOW I'M DOIN' THE RIGHT THING
WALK AWAY FROM ME- GO ON- WALK AWAY FROM ME
GO ON- AFTER ALL I TOLE YOU TO DO IT
I C'N FACE THE HEARTBREAK THE SORROW AN' THE PAIN
I C'N FACE IT LIKE A MAN
EVEN IF I AM ONLY A SMALL BOY FACIN' INCREDIBABBLE ODDS AN' WHOSE BES' FRIEN' HAS JUST WALKED OUT ON HIM LEAVIN' HIM ALONE AN' WHAT'S MORE...
V49
Maurice Dodd
-GOOD OLE BOOT-FAITHFUL TO THE END

D'YOU REMEMBER BRER RABBIT?
WHEN THE FOX CAUGHT HIM HE BEGGED NOT TO BE THROWN IN THE BRIAR-PATCH
SO OF COURSE THE FOX, BEIN' ALMOS' HUMAN, THREW HIM IN THE BRIAR-PATCH
(PSST-WE C'N USE THE SAME PSYCHOLOGY WITH THE WEATHER)
D'YOU SEE WHAT I'M GETTIN' AT, BOOT?
OH I DO-INDEED I DO
AND I'M DAMNED IF I'M GOING TO BE THROWN IN A BRIAR-PATCH
V50
Maurice Dodd

WAIT, BOOT-YOU HAVEN'T GOT THE POINT OF THE BRER-RABBIT STORY
BUT I WILL IF I GET THROWN INTO THE BRIAR-PATCH
BRER-RABBIT WANTED TO BE THROWN INTO THE BRIAR-PATCH YOU SILLY OL' THING -IT'S WHERE HE LIVED
BUT THE FOX DIDN'T KNOW THAT, HE THREW HIM IN OUT OF SPITE
(SO IF WE PRETEND WE'RE ENJOYIN' THIS TERRIBLE WEATHER-IT'LL CHANGE OUT OF SPITE)
OH WE LOVE ALL THIS HORRIBLE WEATHER -LOVE IT-LOVE IT-LOVE IT-AN' WE HOPE IT'LL NEVER GET BETTER
ARF ARF
WHAT WE'VE GOT HERE IS A SEVERE CASE OF WEATHER THAT KNOWS ITS 'UNCLE REMUS'
Maurice Dodd
V51

O'COURSE YOU LOT ARE LAUGHIN'

-SINCE I'M COPPIN' ALL THE BAD WEATHER YOU'RE ALL GETTIN' GOOD WEATHER AN' HAVIN' THE TIME OF YOUR LIVES!
YEA
'RAY
HEY
WHOOPIE
WHAHOO
CHEERS

Y'SEE, BOOT, I WAS RIGHT ABOUT THE WEATHER
IT CAN'T BEAR TOO MANY PEOPLE HAVIN' TOO GOOD A TIME FOR TOO LONG
Maurice Dodd V52

V53
H'LO, BOOT, OLD CHAPS-ANY NEWS FOR THE NEWSHOUND?
NONE AT ALL, B.H. (CALCUTTA) FAILED-ALL IS TRANQUIL HERE
BY JINGO-A BONE!
NOW THERE'S A STORY..
"ACE REPORTER FINDS MISSING BONE"
BY THE LORD HARRY -WHAT A PACK OF ROGUES YOU SCRIVENERS ARE
YOU'LL EVEN STOOP TO COMPLETE FABRICATION IN ORDER TO...
WHERE'S MY BONE?
IT'S MISSING!
Maurice Dodd

HOLD HARD THERE CULLY
UNHAND THAT BONE
FOR SHAME- FOR SHAME WOULDST STAND IN THE PATH OF TRUE LOVE?
TRUE LOVE WHAT TISH-TOSHERY IS THIS?
TOSH-TISHERY?! I LOVE THIS BONE
LOVE IT- LOVE IT-LOVIT LOVITLOVIT!
GRONFF
SLURP
V54
Maurice Dodd

-OOH BY CRIKEY-YOU'RE POSITIVELY GORGEOUS!
BY THUNDER SIRRAH STOP LATHERING THAT BONE WITH LIQUID LUST
THAT IS MY BONE!
Maurice Dodd
YOUR BONE-YOUR BONE?
BY GOLLIES THAT ARE PRETTY HIGH HANDED!
I'LL BET YOU'RE NOT EVEN MARRIED
(DON'T WORRYING- I'LL MAKE AN HONEST BONE OF YOU)
V55

YOU'VE BEEN TAKING ADVANTAGE OF THIS INNOCENT BONE, WITHOUT EVEN A HINT OF MARRIAGE!
MARRIAGE? MARRIAGE?
(FLY WITH ME, BONE, WE'LL CELEBRATE A NIBBLING NUPTIAL)
NOBODY IN THEIR RIGHT MIND WOULD THINK OF MARRYING A BONE
V56
Maurice Dodd

-OOH-YOU UNSPEAKABLE CAD!

DID YOU HEAR THE SENTIMENTS OF THAT CAD, OH FRAIL AND RAVISHED BONE?
HE SAID NOBODY IN THEIR RIGHT MINDS WOULD DREAM OF MARRYING A BONE!
SLURP SLURP
HAVE YOU TAKEN LEAVE OF YOUR SENSES FELLOW?
-TALKING TO A BONE!

LET US FLEE, BONE-LET US FLEE
BEFORE SUCH RAMPANT SNOBBERY REASON CANNOT PREVAIL
V57
Maurice Dodd

BY CRIKEY- WAITING 'TIL I'M GETTING YOU HOME, LOVELY BONE. I'LL THRILL YOU TO YOUR MARROW
SLURP SLURP
Maurice Dodd

FELON, (SNAP) THAT'S THE THIRD TIME YOU'VE ATTEMPTED TO PURLOIN MY BONE!
GURUUU

PURLOIN? -PURLOIN? HOW DARE YOU BRAND ME WITH SO BASE A MOTIVE
-WE'RE ELOPING THIS BONE AND I
V58

LISTEN, B.H. I'VE HAD ENOUGH OF THIS FLIM-FLAMMERY-THIS IS MY BONE AND I'M TAKING IT-NOW
OH? HAVE YOU CONSULTED THE BONE'S WISHES IN THIS REGARD?
Maurice Dodd
V59

AM I LIKELY TO GET AN INTELLIGIBLE ANSWER FROM A BONE?
AHA! NOW I UNDERSTAND YOUR PROBLEM

YOU CAN'T SPEAK BONE- CAN YOU?

YOU DIDN'T ANSWER MY QUESTION, BOOT
YOU CAN'T SPEAK BONE CAN YOU?
SPEAK BONE? COME OFF IT B.H. THERE'S NO SUCH LINGO
OH NO? ALLOW ME TO DEMONSTRATE
V60
REGARDEZ-MOI MA P'TITE, JE T'ADORE PIAT D'OR, TORRI-ADORE LET'S DITCH OLD CARPET-VISAGE ET SCARPER TOUTE SUITE (LICK-LICK)
THAT'S FRENCH
EXACTEMENTS - FRENCH AS SHE IS SPOKE ON THE COTE DE BEAUNE
Maurice Dodd

WELL AS A MATTER OF FACT I CAN PARLAY A LITTLE FRANCAIS MONSELF
TO WIT-SHOVE OFFEZ-VOUS

AND LEAVE MY BONEO ALONEO
SORRY MY MISTAKE THAT WAS SPANISH
Maurice Dodd
V61

HANGING ABOUT BOOT OLD CHAPS, I HAVEN'T TOLD YOU ABOUT MY FIVE -STAR BONE-CARE SERVICE
COMPETITIVE RATES FOR TAKING BONES FOR WALKS - WASHING & POLISHING - PIANO-LESSONS... (LICK-LICK)
THUNDERATION, BH, D'YOU WANT TO END UP BAD FRIENDS WITH ME?
Maurice Dodd
V62

ER.. WOULD THAT BE WITH OR WITHOUT THE BONE? (LICK-LICK)

LOOKING HERE, BOOT, AREN'T YOU BEING RATHER DOG-IN-THE -MANGER WITH REGARD TO THIS BONE?
Maurice Dodd
DOG IN THE MANGER?
LOOK TO YOUR OWN CONDUCT SIRRAH
ENVIOUS AVARICIOUS, DEVIOUS IMPORTUNING AND MUCH MORE BESIDES
HMM (SNIFF) AT LEAST I DON'T SPEAK WITH MY MOUTH FULL
V63

WELL IF YOU'RE DETERMINED TO CLAIM THAT ENTIRE BONE FOR YOURSELF-MAY I BE PERMITTED TO MAKE MY FAREWELLS? (LICK LICK)
OH VERY WELL-BUT FROM A SAFE DISTANCE -STEP BACK A FEW PACES

MORE-A FEW PACES MORE
MauriceDodd

MORE-MORE -MUCH MORE-EVEN MORE
V64

I THINK, IN THE CIRCUMSTANCES, I'LL SEND IT A FAREWELL NOTE

I FEEL GUILTY NOW -NOT LETTING B. H. SHARE MY BONE
MauriceDodd

MEAN AND GUILTY AND CONTEMPTIBLE
DAMMIT ALL-WHEN IT COMES DOWN TO IT I COULD HAVE GIVEN HIM THE WRETCHED THING
V65

OH DEAR-IT LOOKS AS IF I'M GOING TO HAVE TO WRESTLE WITH MY CONSCIENCE...
-HERE GOES THEN
GRRRRR
GRRRR
GRRRR

-THANK GOODNESS I WON

BOOT- I THINK IT'S ABOUT TIME FOR THE ANNUAL BATH
V66

SNIFF SNIFF SNIFF SNIFF SNIFF

SNIFF SNIFF SNIFF SNIFF SNIFF
!

-I'D SAY YOU WE'RE ABOUT RIGHT
MauriceDodd

LOOK, BOOT, WHEN I SAID IT WAS TIME FOR THE ANNUAL BATH I WAS TALKING ABOUT YOU NOT ME
MauriceDodd
V67

AN' IT'S NO USE YOU TRYIN' TO HIDE
D'YOU THINK I CAN'T SEE YOU UNDER THERE?

CONCEALMENT WAS NOT MY PRIMARY PURPOSE
IMMOVABILITY WAS MORE WHAT I HAD IN MIND

WHEN I SAY YOU'RE GOIN' TO HAVE A BATH - BELIEVE ME YOU'RE GOIN' TO HAVE A BATH
V68

SO - DETERMINED TO GET YOUR OWN WAY ARE YOU?
WELL TWO OF US C'N PLAY AT THAT GAME!

ONE OF US ISN'T VERY GOOD AT IT
Maurice Dodd

JUS' HOW FAR D'YOU THINK THIS WILL GET YOU?

HE-E-E-Y UP!
WELL - IF YOU MEAN VIEWED AS A MODE OF TRANSPORT
V69

IT DOES LACK A DEGREE OF EFFICIENCY
BUT IT IS A PROTOTYPE
Maurice Dodd

- WE CAN MAKE MODIFICATIONS AT A LATER DATE

COR
PUFF
CRUMBS

AAAGH
-SEE WHAT YOU'VE DONE HERE-JUS' SEE WHAT YOU'VE DONE!

D'YOU WISH ME TO MAKE A TOUR OF INSPECTION OR WILL A CURSORY GLANCE SUFFICE?
V70
Maurice Dodd

THIS HAS GONE FAR ENOUGH

YOU'RE GOIN' TO HAVE A BATH AN' WE'RE NOT GOIN' IN FOR ANY MORE OLE NONSENSE ARE WE?

WELL I HAVE NOTHING OF THAT NATURE PLANNED
URK!

BUT I'M NOT AT ALL CERTAIN I CAN SPEAK FOR YOU
V71
Maurice Dodd

HELP-HELP-
GET THIS ROTTEN
THING OFF
MY HEAD
V72

HEARING
HIS MASTER'S CRY
OF DISTRESS THE NOBLE
DOG DASHES TO
THE RESCUE

OOOOOOF!

WILL THE
NOBLE DOG EVER
LEARN TO LEAVE WELL
ENOUGH ALONE?
Maurice Dodd

AH-HA
NOW I'VE
GOT YOU!
V73
NOW HE'S
GOT ME? WHAT
CAN THAT
PORTEND?
SURELY
HE'D NOT TAKE
ADVANTAGE
OF A POOR
OLD DOG IN
THRALL TO
SUCH CRUEL
HAPPENSTANCE
ONLY
A ROTTER
WOULD DO
SUCH A
THING
I SAID
YOU WERE GOIN'
TO HAVE A BATH
AN YOU'RE
GOIN' TO
HAVE A
BATH
AN INGENIOUS
LITTLE ROTTER
ISN'T HE?
Maurice Dodd

SO YOU DIN'T WANT TO HAVE A BATH A? WELL, WHADDAYA THINK OF THAT?
V74
AN' HOW ABOUT THAT THEN, WHADDAYA THINK OF THAT?
WELL FOR ONE THING I'M BEGINNING TO DOUBT IF THESE CONSTANT REQUESTS FOR MY OPINION ARE IN ANY WAY GENUINE
MauriceDodd

WELL MR DON'T-WANNA HAVE-A-BATH I'D LIKE TO KNOW WHAT YOU THINK OF THAT
MauriceDodd
V75

PFOOF
AND I, IN TURN, WOULD VALUE YOUR OPINION ON THIS
I'M AFRAID OOF-PUFF-SPLUTTER AND BLOB ARE HARDLY TERMS WHICH I CAN EVALUATE

WELLIN'TON, **WELLIN'TON**, ARE YOU COMIN' OUT TO PLAY?
Maurice Dodd

V76

DOES THAT MEAN **YES** OR **NO**?
FRONT

WELLIN'TON- WHAT'S GOIN' ON?
I WANT T'KNOW WHAT'S GOIN' ON?
Maurice Dodd
V77

SLAM
WHA' HAPPENED- WHA' HAPPENED?
YOU WOULD'N' BELIEVE ME IF I TOLE YOU

ENOUGH'S ENOUGH. I'M GOIN' TO GET THIS ROTTEN THING OFF YOUR HEAD
EVEN IF IT-
V78

-KILLS ME

CRASH
NOW SEE WHAT'S HAPPENED!

OH IT COULDN'T,
COULD IT?
YOU NEVER KNOW-MAYBE IT...
YOU'VE DONE IT AGAIN, ANOTHER MESS YOU'VE GOT ME INTO

THAT ROTTEN HORN COULD'VE BEEN STUCK ON MY HEAD
- AND ANOTHER ASPIRATION BITES THE DUST!
Maurice Dodd

JUS' LOOK
LOOK AT THE MESS IN THIS PLACE
WHAT'M I GOIN' TO DO?
BANG
BANG
BANG
Maurice Dodd

WELLIN'TON- WHAT'S GOIN' ON IN THERE?
WHAT'RE YOU UP TO? I WANNA KNOW
I S'POSE YOU THINK THAT'S FUNNY
V79

IT'S STUCK FAST
THIS ROTTEN THING'S STUCK FAST
D'YOU HEAR ME, MARLON?
MARLON
ARE YOU THERE?
SAY SOMETHIN' -WHY DON'T YOU SAY SOMETHIN'?
W-E-L-L...
WHADDAYA MEAN-YOU THINK IT SUITS ME?
Maurice Dodd
V80

DON'T JUS' STAN' THERE, MARLON
THINK OF A WAY TO GET THIS THING OFF MY HEAD
OIL
A?
IF I POUR OIL DOWN THE TOP IT'LL MAKE YOU ALL SLIPPERY AN'...
HOW STUPID - HOW TOTALLY STUPID
I'LL BET EVEN YOU CAN'T THINK OF ANYTHIN' MORE STUPID THAN THAT
ER... -TREACLE?
Maurice Dodd
V81

AAGH!
OUCH!
OOOH!
BRACE Y'SELF, MAISIE - BRACE Y'SELF
Maurice Dodd
YOU COULD'VE BEEN A BIT MORE GENTLE
V82
YOU ALMOS' TORE MY HEAD OFF AN' YOU'VE MADE MY HAIR A RIGHT MESS. YOU'VE GOT AS MUCH CONSIDERATION AS A -
IF THERE'S ONE THING I CAN'T STAN' IT'S PETTY-MINDED PEOPLE

LISTEN, MAISIE - I'VE DONE MY BEST TO 'ELP YOU
AN' ALL I'VE 'AD IN RETURN IS A LOAD OF THE OLE VERBALS
FRONT
Maurice Dodd
-YOU'LL GET NO MORE 'ELP FROM ME UNLESS I GET AN APOLOGY
HELP? POO -WHO NEEDS HELP? I C'N DO WITHOUT YOUR HELP THANK YOU
FRONT
V83
SO WHADDAYA THINK OF THAT THEN, MARLON - WHADDAYA THINK OF THAT?
FRONT

LISTEN, MAISIE-YOU'RE IN DEAD TROUBLE YOU ARE
ALL Y'GOTTA DO IS SAY SORRY FOR BEIN' SUCH A PAIN-AN' I'LL GET YOU 'OME
SORRY? SORRY? THAT'LL BE THE DAY!
I'LL NEVER COME CRAWLIN' TO YOU-NEVER -NEVER EVER
OR MY NAME'S NOT MAISIE
YES-YES-ALL-RIGHT-I'LL BE YOUR WILLIN' SLAVE-AN' I'LL GIVE YOU MY SWEETIES--AN'-ALL THEM OTHER THINGS
THAT'S MORE LIKE IT, PRISCILLA
Maurice Dodd
V84

AM I NEARLY HOME, MARLON?
YEA-'ERE WE ARE, MAISIE -TUMBRIL TERRACE
BUT I'M NOT GOIN' TO STICK AROUN' -EXPLAININ' TO YOUR MUM..
I'M JUS' GOIN' TO KNOCK AN' LEG IT
FRONT
OOOW MUM- LOOK WHAT THEY DID TO ME, MUM-IT'S BEEN-TERRIBLE, MUM -MUM? MUM? WHY DON'T YOU ANSWER ME, MUM?
A? WHICH? WOT? OO'RE YOU? WOT'S GOIN' ON?! I'LL CALL THE P'LICE...
THAT'S FUNNY-I COULD'VE SWORN THAT WAS TUMBRIL TERRACE
UMBRIL TERRACE
Maurice Dodd
V85

..."it wasn't me who put glue on the loo-seat, maisie"
no-no that won't do...
..."there's been an unfortunate accident involving a quantity of glue and the loo seat"
or maybe- "you may have noticed something different about the loo-seat"
maisie- i've got something to tell you
KNOCK KNOCK
WHAT IS IT - BABY GRUMPLIN'?
well, should mi tale surprise you-don't try to get up suddenly
Maurice Dodd
V86

d'you know what, gladly, they're threatening to send me to play-school!
i mean- play school!
why play-school?
who needs play-school?
i'm already totally efficient at playing
V87
Maurice Dodd

ARE YOU ALL READY FOR YOUR FIRST DAY AT PLAY-SCHOOL TOMORROW, BABY GRUMPLIN?
no-i am not
-and has anybody thought about the teachers' strike?
BUT THERE ISN'T A TEACHERS' STRIKE AT PLAY-SCHOOL
don't worry there soon will be;
V88
Maurice Dodd

I'M GLAD TO SEE YOU'RE FACIN' UP TO STARTIN' PLAY-SCHOOL LIKE A MAN, BABY GRUMPLIN'
well-maisie, i thought it was expected of me
to go bravely forth and face the unknown with firm tread and head held high
-on the other hand there is an alternative
Maurice Dodd
V89

BABY GRUMPLIN'?
WHAT HAPPENED- WHAT HAPPENED AT PLAY-SCHOOL?
we were introduced to the play -tunnel
and in my opinion that play-school lacks adequate supervision
MauriceDodd
V90

WHAT WAS YOUR FIRST DAY AT PLAY-SCHOOL LIKE, BABY GRUMPLING?
terrible - i'm totally disillusioned
i'll never believe anything anybody ever tells me again
OH, WHY IS THAT?
well-they promised us toad-in-the-hole for lunch
and all we got was some sausages stuck in a batter-pudding!
V91
MauriceDodd

WHAT ELSE HAPPENED AT PLAY-SCHOOL BABY GRUMPLIN'?
well, some woman showed us how she cut shapes from sheets of coloured paper
and pasted them onto bits of cardboard
frankly i was astonished at such infantile behaviour
Maurice Dodd
V92

I'M ALL SET FOR THE MAY-QUEEN ELECTIONS
RIGHT-PADDED HOCKEY-STICK, TOFFEES FOR BRIBES, PRE-FILLED VOTIN' FORMS...
why not rely on the democratic process, maisie?
why not present your credentials and let people freely vote you in?
V93
Maurice Dodd

I WILL NOT ENCOURAGE GAMBLIN'

WHO ARE YOU THINKIN' OF VOTIN' FOR AS MAY-QUEEN, MARLON?
OW... ER... BLOSSOM McGINSBERG
BLOSSOM McGINSBERG? NAME ONE THING SHE'S GOT THAT I HAVEN'T
WELL- SHE'S PRETTY AN' SMELLS NICE AN' SHE'S GOOD FUN AN'....
-IF I'D KNOWN YOU COULD COUNT PAST ONE I WOULD'N' HAVE ASKED
FRONT
Maurice Dodd
V94

D'YOU REALLY THINK THAT 'ORRIBLE BLOSSOM McGINSBERG WILL MAKE A BETTER LOOKIN' MAY-QUEEN THAN ME?
C'MON- I WANT A STRAIGHT SINCERE ANSWER
WELL IF YOU MUS' KNOW-YES
NOW LET'S TRY ONE OF THE CROOKED AN' TOTALLY INSINCERE KIND
FRONT
V95
Maurice Dodd

V96
-SO YOU TWO ARE GOIN' TO VOTE FOR BLOSSOM McGINSBERG AS MAY-QUEEN
JUS' COS' YOU THINK SHE'S PRETTY AN' SWEET NATURED AN' STUFF
Maurice Dodd
WELL DID YOU KNOW SHE'S BALD AN' WEARS A WIG?
AN' SHE DROWNS KITTENS AN' PULLS THE WINGS OFF FLIES
I DIN'T KNOW ANY OF THAT
NOR DID I UNTIL A FEW MINUTES AGO
CERTAINLY NOT
YOU MEAN YOU LIED?
I'LL ADMIT TO MAKIN' A WILD GUESS

BERYL BOGEY'S MY ELECTION AGENT
URK URK
SHE'S GOIN' TO SHAKE UP THE ELECTORATE
AN' WE'RE GOIN' FOR PROPORTIONAL REPRESENTATION
Maurice Dodd
V97
-IF YOU DON'T VOTE FOR ME SHE'LL ALTER YOUR PROPORTIONS!
URK URK URK
GAH

LOOK HERE, MAISIE - WE'RE NOT GOIN' T'BE INTIMIDATED BY BERYL BOGEY
YEA - WERE CALLIN' YOUR BLUFF
ONE MOMENT PLEASE
VOTE FOR MAISIE
Maurice Dodd
URK-URK-URK
HERE Y'ARE BERYL - HAVE A MOUSE
GLOP
RIGHT - NOW THAT LUNCH-BREAK'S OVER....
VOTE FOR MAISIE
V98

YOU STAY AWAY FROM US, MAISIE
'LO BOYS - NOW ABOUT ME BEIN' ELECTED MAY-QUEEN
YEA - YOU OUGHTA BE ASHAMED
FRONT
V99
Maurice Dodd
WHY - WHAT'VE I DONE?
WHAT HAVEN'T YOU DONE?
YOU'VE TRIED VOTE-RIGGIN' - CHEATIN', LYIN', INTIMERDATION - EVERYTHIN' BUT BRIBERY
FRONT
I KNOW - I KNOW - YOU'RE RIGHT OF COURSE
- BUT I CAN'T POSSIBLY AFFORD BRIBERY
FRONT

THERE'S SAFETY IN NUMBERS-RIGHT, MARLON?
RIGHT, WELLIN'TON
ER... YOU ARE GOIN' T'BE OUR SPOKESMAN AREN'T YOU?
LISTEN, MAISIE, WE'RE FED-UP WITH YOU'N BERYL BOGEY TELLIN' US HOW WE'RE GOIN' TO VOTE
AN' THERE'S A LOT OF US
WHAT'VE YOU GOT TO SAY ABOUT THAT?
-NEXT...
FRON
TER
V100

THAT WAS A SUPER-BRILL IDEA OF YOURS, WELLIN'TON- ASKIN' FOR A POSTAL VOTE TO ELECT THE MAY-QUEEN
YEA - I CAN'T WAIT TO SEE MAISIE'S FACE
HERE SHE COMES NOW
WELL WHEN I FIND OUT WHO ASKED FOR A POSTAL VOTE-THERE'S GOIN' T'BE TROUBLE
BIG TROUBLE
WHERE ARE YOU GOIN' TO POST YOUR VOTE FROM?
AUSTRALIA
FRONT
Maurice Dodd
V101

I'M NOT HAVIN' ANY OF THIS SNEAKY HOLE-IN-THE -CORNER SECRET BALLOT FOR THE MAY-QUEEN ELECTION
I WANT A GOOD OLE OUT-IN-THE-OPEN SHOW OF HAN'S
URK URK URK
CAMPANE HQ
THAT TOLD'M-A BERYL?
MauriceDodd
V102

NOW LET'S GET PRACTICIN' AT SHOWIN' HAN'S

V103
RIGHT, CHILDREN-WE'RE GOING TO ELECT OUR MAY-QUEEN BY SHOW OF HANDS
-ALL THOSE IN FAVOUR OF BLOSSOM McGINSBERG
WELL, MAISIE-THAT SEEMS PRETTY CONCLUSIVE
HANG ABOUT MISS-YOU HAVEN'T SEEN MY SHOW OF HAN'S
OK-BERYL AN FRIEN'S-LET'S SEE IT FOR MAISIE!
OK-OK-WHO'S THE JOKER?
MD

MAISIE I'M SORRY YOU DIDN'T GET TO BE MAY-QUEEN BUT YOU MUSTN'T BE TOO UPSET
UPSET? OH, POO, MUM- WHAT MAKES YOU THINK I'M UPSET?
MAI FOR QUEE
-JUS' COS A GIRL DECIDES TO SPEND A QUIET DAY IN THE CUPBOARD WHY SHOULD EVERYBODY THINK SHE'S (GRRR GNASH SPIT) UPSET?
Maurice Dodd V104

WELL- WHAT DID YOU DO TODAY AT PLAY-SCHOOL?
we had 'gluing'
-it's mi fervent hope that tomorrow we'll have 'ungluing'
Maurice Dodd
V105

WHAT'S THIS, MARLON, ARE YOU TRAININ' FOR THE SPORTS-DAY GYMNASTICS ?
Maurice Dodd

NO - I'M STUDYIN' THE LIST OF EVENTS

-SOME FOOL'S PINNED 'EM UP UPSIDE-DOWN
FOUND
V106

MARLON- ARE YOU GOIN' IN FOR THE DECATHLON?
OW ER-YEA
O'COURSE
WELL I WOULD- WOULDN'I ?
OOOOOH!
OOH-HE'S SO BRAVE
AN' HAN'SOME
OH I LOVE A MAN TO BE A MAN DON'T YOU?
V107
ER WELLIN'TON? THIS DEE-CAFLON THING
D'YOU RUN IT, JUMP IT, THROW IT, PUSH IT OR WOT ?
Maurice Dodd

PLACE Y'R BETS - PLACE Y'R BETS FOR THE EGG'N'SPOON RACE
ARE YOU THINKIN' OF HAVIN' A FLUTTER ON THE EGG'N' SPOON, MARLON?
RIGHT, MAISIE, I'VE GOTTER GOOD IDEA OF 'OOS GOIN' T'WIN
-I'LL 'AVE 10p ON THE EGG
FRONT
Maurice Dodd
V108

I'M GLAD TO SEE YOU'VE PUT YOUR NAME DOWN FOR A NUMBER OF EVENTS, MAISIE
-FACING GOOD HONEST COMPETITION
FAIR N'SQUARE
OUT IN THE OPEN FOR ALL TO SEE
OI-HANG ABOUT
-ARE THEY THE ONLY OPTIONS?
Maurice Dodd
V109

- AND FOR THE NEXT HEAT OF THE HUNDRED METRES...
I WONDER WHY THEY CALL'M HEATS?
Maurice Dodd

WELL I S'POSE IT'S COS THE MORE'V 'EM YOU DO THE 'OTTER AN' SWEATIER AN' STICKIER YOU GET AN'...
I WISH I HADN'T ASKED
V110

THEY'RE LINED UP FOR THE HUNDRED METRES
AND THEY'RE OFF
Maurice Dodd
V111
DIRTY Mc SQUIRTY'S ALREADY TAKEN THE LEAD
WHICH HE'S INCREASING AT AN ASTONISHING RATE!
-ALL THE REST ARE RUNNING THE OTHER WAY

CONTESTANTS LINE UP FOR THE EGG AND SPOON RACE
ER... MAR-LON
YOU SHOULDN' TIE YOUR EGG TO YOUR SPOON
-IT'S THE ONLY PRACTICAL WAY MAISIE BELIEVE ME
I CAN'T GLUE IT COS I WOULDN' BE ABLE TO GET IT OFF AGAIN, AN' I TRIED NAILIN' IT BUT
YOU SHOULDN' FIX IT ON IN ANY WAY WHATSO-EVER
TALK SENSE - IF I DON'T FIX IT IT'LL FALL OFF
THERE ARE TIMES WHEN YOU SURPRISE ME
Maurice Dodd
V112

...AND THE NEXT EVENT WILL BE THE GREAT FLY RACE - THE WINNING FLY WILL RECEIVE.. FLY RACE? - WHO PUT THIS IN?
DON'T LOOK AT ME - YOU'RE IN CHARGE OF ENTRIES
IF THIS IS ONE OF YOUR PRACTICAL JOKES YOU LOONY...
LOONY? HOW DARE YOU - YOU TOFFEE-NOSED OLD HAYBAG
I'LL GIVE YOU HAYBAG YOU FEATHER BRAINED LITTLE TART
DON'T YOU COME NEAR ME YOU HAG FACED OLD SHRIEK
WAIT FOR IT - WAIT FOR IT - WAIT FOR THE STARTING PISTOL
Maurice Dodd
V113

CONTESTANTS LINE-UP FOR THE SACK-RACE
Maurice Dodd
ER. MARLON...
V114

-IT'S A TOTALLY BRILL IDEA -A SPRING ASSISTED POLE FOR THE POLE-VAULT
COR. WELLIN'TON C'N I BE THE FIRS' TO GIVE IT A GO?
IT'S ASTONISHIN' HOW NOBODY'S THOUGHT OF IT BEFORE
IT DOESN' WORK, DOES IT?
Maurice Dodd
V115

I SHOULD'VE KNOWN BETTER THAN TO LET YOU TRY OUT MY SPRING-LOADED POLE-VAULT ASSISTERATOR, MARLON
Maurice Dodd
SINCE YOU MANAGE TO MAKE A MESS OF JUS' ABOUT EVERYTHIN' YOU DO
V116
IS THERE
A CATEGORY
FOR THE HEAD HOP?

HELP, MARLÓN, HELP
Maurice Dodd
LOOK AT THIS THING
LOOK AT THIS ROTTEN THING ON MY HEAD
V117
HMM
COR
OUCH
PUFF
GROAN
GASP
OOOH
-STUCK INNIT?

STUCK?
O'COURSE IT'S STUCK
HERE'M I WITH THIS ROTTEN SPRING WEDGED ON MY HEAD AN' ALL YOU C'N SAY IS IT'S STUCK!
I LOOK A RIGHT NANA -CAN'T YOU DO SOMETHIN'?
SOMETHIN' PRACTICAL
Maurice Dodd
'ANG ABOUT
V118
HMM
'OW ABOUT A BIGGER 'AT?

WELLIN'TON- I RECKON BERYL BOGEY C'N GET THAT SPRING OFF YOUR BONCE
GIVE IT THE OLE HEAVE HO, BERYL
URK URK URK
I DON'T THINK THIS IS
GETTIN' ME VERY FAR
V119
MD

HEAVE
HEAVE
HEAVE
HEAVE
I DON'T LIKE THIS-WHAT IF WE PULLED HIS HEAD OFF?
I THINK IT'D COUNT AS A WIN FOR THE OTHER TEAM
V120
Maurice Dodd

HEAVE
HEAVE
V121
BOING
Maurice Dodd
OH, CRUMBS THANKS-THANKS ALL OF YOU-HOW CAN I EVER THANK YOU ENOUGH?
S'AL'RIGHT, WELLINTON
THINK NOTHIN' OF IT
W-E-L-L...
A TRIP TO THE FLICKS MIGHT GO SOMEWHERE TOWARDS IT
AN' A BOX OF CHOCS WOULD BE NICE
AN' THERE'S THAT ALBUM I'VE WANTED AN' I'VE SEEN THE CUTEST...

LOOK, WELLIN'TON- LOOK
I'M PUTTIN' THE SHOT
Maurice Dodd
V122

WOULD YOU VERY MUCH MIND PUTTIN' IT SOMEWHERE ELSE?

WELL I RECKON WE'VE GOT ONE RACE IN THE BAG, MARLON
AN', THAT'S THIS RELAY
Maurice Dodd

PUFF PANT GASP
WHO PUT DIRTY Mc SQUIRTY IN THE TEAM?
V123

ER, MARLON
V124

WOT IS IT, MAISIE?

OH- NEVER MIND

I WAS ONLY GOIN' TO REMIND YOU Y'HAVTA LET GO OF THAT THING
Maurice Dodd

ARE THE SPORTS EVENTS OVER?
Y'COULD SAY THAT
Maurice Dodd
V125

BUT THEY'RE MORE OVER FOR SOME THAN FOR OTHERS

HI, BOOT-THE SCHOOL SPORTS ARE OVER
I'VE COME TO TAKE YOU WITH ME TO THE FETE
V126
COR-IT'S GOIN' T'BE GREAT
THEY'VE GOT SWING-BOATS AN' DODGEMS AN' ROCKET CHAIRS
AN' DONKEY-RIDES AN' BREAK-THE CROCKERY STALL

I C'N SEE YOU C'N HARDLY STOP YAWNIN' WITH EXCITEMENT
Maurice Dodd

IT'S A SMASHIN' FETE, BOOT, YOU'LL LOVE IT
WHAT WITH ALL THE SWINGS'N' RIDES'N' GAMES 'N' SLIDES
OH YOU PAINT A PRETTY PICTURE, QUITE LYRICAL IN PARTS
Maurice Dodd

OF PARTICULAR NOTE IS THE PASSAGE-'SWINGS 'N' RIDES 'N' GAMES 'N' SLIDES'

...I'LL WAGER THERE'S NOT A DAMN THING THERE WHICH RHYMES WITH 'BONES'
V127

WAIT'LL YOU SEE THE STUFF AT THE FETE, BOOT. DODGEMS. SLIDES, AN' ALL SORTS OF STALLS
MauriceDodd
V128
PLENTY OF GRUB TOO - HAMBURGERS SAUSAGES AN' THERE'S A PIE STALL

HEY - HANG ABOUT - WHAT'S GOT INTO YOU?
IT'S MORE A MATTER OF WHAT'S GOING TO GET INTO ME - WITH ANY LUCK

WHERE'S MARLON?
ON THE HELTER-SKELTER

AN' I THINK HE SKELTERED WHEN HE SHOULD'VE HELTERED
V129
MauriceDodd

GHOST TRAIN

WELL? WHAT WAS IT LIKE?
V130

WHY DO THEY CALL IT A *COCONUT SHY*?
IT OBVIOUSLY REFERS TO A CHARACTER TRAIT
V131
DEVELOPED THROUGH BEIN' CONSTANTLY CLOUTED BY EXTREMELY HARD WOODEN BALLS
Maurice Dodd

BERYL BOGEY'S GOIN' ON THE GHOST TRAIN
COR ! CAN'T WAIT TO SEE HER COMIN'...
...OUT
URK URK URK
AAAAGH
FRONT
Maurice Dodd
V132

BREAK THE CROCKERY 20p
THAT'S WHAT MAISIE'S BEEN SAVIN' HERSELF FOR
THE ! BREAK-THE-CROCKERY STALL
COR- REMEMBER THE CHASSIS SHE CAUSED LAS' TIME ?
VIVIDLY
CLEAR OFF
GET OUT OF IT
AN' SO, APPARENTLY, DO THE STALL-HOLDERS
V133
Maurice Dodd

ENJOYIN' Y'SELF, MAISIE?
WELL- I'M IN TWO MINDS

MAYBE ON THE WAY UP

DEFINITELY NOT ON THE WAY DOWN
V134
MD

HOOPLA
FANCY A GO ON THE HOOPLA, MARLON?
NO THANKS, MAISIE
FRONT
Maurice Dodd
V135

I WOULD'N' KNOW WHAT TO DO WITH A 'LA' EVEN IF I HOOPED ONE
FRONT

YOO-HOO, MARLON-FANCY COMIN' IN THE TUNNEL OF LOVE?
FRONT
Maurice Dodd

TUNEL OF LOVE FREE!
IT DON'T LOOK VERY WIDE

NEVER MIND THE WIDTH -FEEL THE QUALITY
AWK
FREE
SQUIRP
SQUIRP
SQUIRP
V136

TRAMPOLINES
½hr for 50p
WHEEE
H-E-E-E-Y
WHOO
URK-URK
-URK-URK
-URK
Maurice Dodd
V137

C'MON, BOOT -HAVE A GO ON THE TRAMPOLINE
MauriceDodd
V138
YOU'RE NOT VERY GOOD AT HIDIN' YOUR FEELIN'S ARE YOU?

I THOUGHT YOU WERE AFRAID TO GO ON THE GHOST-TRAIN, MAISIE
YEA-BUT NOT WHEN BERYL BOGEY'S WITH ME
MauriceDodd

WHERE'S BERYL?
THEY MADE HER AN OFFER SHE COULD'N' REFUSE
V139

OH WHAT'S THE **POINT** OF IT ALL?
THIS TINSEL TAWDRYNESS THIS GIGGLIN' GRASPIN' FOR EMPTY PLEASURE AN' EXCITEMENT
ENOUGH-I TURN MY BACK ON IT-I'LL PLAY THE FOOL NO MORE
V140

RUN OUT OF MONEY FOR THE RIDES?
YOU'VE GOT IT
Maurice Dodd

WELL IT'S BEEN A GREAT DAY HAS'N' IT, BOOT?
-A GOOD TIME WAS HAD BY ONE AN' ALL
V141
OH - UNDOUBTEDLY SO
WITH THE EXCEPTION OF THE BOY WHO CATAPULTED OFF THE SWING-BOAT
Maurice Dodd
-AND THE GIRL WHO WAS MISTAKEN FOR A COCONUT
-AND THE LASS WITH A TOAD IN HER TIGHTS
-AND THE LAD WHO HAD A JELLIED -EEL RAMMED UP HIS NOSE
-AND THE KID WHO FELL INTO THE TEA-URN
AND THE CHILD WHO GOT A TOE TRAPPED IN THE TRAMPOLINE

WHAT'VE YOU GOT THERE, BABY GRUMPLIN'?
a worm pie
it's very nourishing- tastes good too
see?
OH-DON'T N-O-O-O-O-O
AH-OOH-EEEEEE SHRIEK
what strange behaviour...
just because i've cooked up a little snack for the worms!
GAH
Maurice Dodd
V142

G'MORNING, BH- WHAT A GLORIOUS DAY
REDOLENT WITH THE SMELLS OF SUMMER WAFTING OVER THE BALMY BREEZE
ALAS BOOT YOU FORGET- I'M HAVING ABSOLUTELY NO SENSE OF SMELL
OH, THAT'S RIGHT - AN UNFORTUNATE ACCIDENT WAS IT NOT?
DURING THE FINALS FOR MY BLOOD-HOUND EXAMS
-WHEN THEY FILLED AN ELEPHANT WITH CURRY AND TURNED HIM LOOSE IN THE MID-DAY SUN
INSTRUCTING ME TO FOLLOW HIS TRAIL INTO CALCUTTA
AND DID YOU?
YES-DOGGEDLY FIGHTING MY WAY AGAINST THE MOB
THE MOB?
YES- AS THE ELEPHANT RAN INTO CALCUTTA EVERYBODY ELSE RAN OUT!
V143
Maurice Dodd

-SO YOU WERE FOLLOWING A CURRY-CRAMMED ELEPHANT
ON A HOT DAY IN CALCUTTA
WHAT HAPPENED NEXT ?
THE SUN'S RAYS EXPANDED THE CURRY TO A GREATER VOLUME THAN THE PACHYDERM COULD CONTAIN...
WELL- YOU'VE HEARD OF THE BIG-BANG THEORY?
ER...IT'S AN ASTRONOMICAL CONCEPT-HAVING SOMETHING TO DO WITH THE EXPANDING UNIVERSE
IN THIS CASE IT HAD A LOT TO DO WITH AN EXPANDING ELEPHANT
V144
Maurice Dodd

D'YOU MEAN THE CURRY-CRAMMED ELEPHANT EXPLODED?
YES, JUST AS I WERE CLOSING IN ON HIM

ALL THEY EVER FOUND WERE HIS TAIL...
...TWO WEEKS LATER...
V145
Maurice Dodd

...WHEN THEY TOOK THE BANDAGES OFF
-IT WERE UP MY NOSE

SO THE ELEPHANT EXPLODED
LITERALLY IN YOUR FACE
AND TWO WEEKS LATER THEY FOUND HIS TAIL
-RAMMED UP YOUR NOSE
- AND YOU THINK THAT ELEPHANT'S TAIL RUINED YOUR SENSE OF SMELL?
Maurice Dodd
WELL-HE WERE A VERY RIPE OLD ELEPHANT
AND HE'D BEEN WEARING IT FOR SOME CONSIDERABLE TIME
V146

RIGHT B.H.-I'VE DECIDED TO HELP YOU RECOVER YOUR OLFACTORY FACILITIES
A WEIGHTY DECISION BY THE FEEL OF IT!
-YOU SEE BEFORE YOU A WELL-WORN WELLINGTON BOOT
IT'S SEEN MORE SERVICE THAN THE GREAT DUKE HIMSELF
V147
ALL I WANT YOU TO DO IS STICK YOUR NOSE IN IT
I CAN'T- IT'S FIXED TO THE END OF MY FACE
Maurice Dodd

I KNOW YOUR NOSE IS FIXED TO THE END OF YOUR FACE-IT'S SUPPOSED TO BE
OTHERWISE IT'D BE RUNNING OFF-STICKING ITSELF INTO OTHER PEOPLE'S BUSINESS
Maurice Dodd V148
OOH, BUT IT DOES RUN
NOT OFF BUT IT DEFINITELY RUNS
I'VE KNOWN IT TO RUN FOR DAYS ON END AND...
I'M NOT HERE TO DISCUSS YOUR RUNNY NOSE
AH - WHAT ARE WE HERE FOR? THAT'S ONE OF LIFE'S GREAT...
GRRRRR
OH... NOT INTERESTED IN PHILOSOPHY EITHER THEN?

WHAT I'M HERE FOR IS TO REHABILITATE YOUR SENSE OF SMELL
I WANT YOU TO STICK YOUR FACE, NOSE FIRST, INTO THAT BOOT
OH, LOOK - I'M PREPARED TO MAKE SACRIFICES
Maurice Dodd

-BUT I'M NOT GOING TO APPEAR IN PUBLIC WEARING THAT RIDICULOUS THING ON MY HEAD
V149

I'M NOT ASKING YOU TO WEAR THIS BLASTED BOOT
I JUST WANT YOU TO STICK YOUR FACE IN AND SMELL IT
ALL RIGHT-BUT YOU FIRST
Maurice Dodd
V150

WHAT?
YOU INSERT YOUR FACE FIRST-TO PROVE THIS ISN'T AN ELABORATE HOAX

OH - VERY WELL

YOU MUST THINK I'M MAD

BY GOLLIES THAT ARE AN ACTION-PACKED PIECE OF FOOTWEAR
WHAT HAVE BEEN IN IT?
V151
FEET
BY CRIKIES - WHAT SORT OF FEET?

YOUNG. MALE. HOMO SAPIENS...
- SAY NO MORE
MD

LOOK, BH · I KNOW THAT FOOTWEAR EXUDES A POTENT PONG
BUT THE EFFECT WILL BE MOLLIFIED BY YOUR DEFECTIVE SENSE OF SMELL
SO GO ON-STICK YOUR FACE IN IT
OH VERY WELL ARE YOU SURE NO HARM WILL BE COMING TO ME?
ABSOLUTELY CERTAIN
ALMOST
ER..
-ANY LAST WORDS?
V152
Maurice Dodd

WELL-SMELL ANYTHING?
NO
BY THE LORD HARRY THAT'S A SPECIMEN OF YOUNG WELLINGTON'S ODORIFEROUS FOOTWEAR AT THE PEAK OF IT'S PONGY POTENTIAL
IT PASSED THE POINT OF MERE RIPE MATURITY YEARS AGO
-WE HAD TO GET IT OFF HIM WITH TYRE-LEVERS
AND YET YOU FEEL NO EFFECT?
THAT ARE BEING THE CASE
YOU'RE NOT BY ANY CHANCE RECENTLY DECEASED ARE YOU?
Maurice Dodd
V153

WELL SINCE THE GUMBOOT REGISTERED NAUGHT ON YOUR PROBOSCOMETER BH. WE MUST TRY ANOTHER TACK
AH- THERE IT IS
Maurice Dodd
WHAT IS IT?
A KIPPER - IT'S A FISH
V154
A FISH?

IT ARE HAVING A VERY POOR SENSE OF DIRECTION !

THIS KIPPER ARE A VERY PECULIAR FISH
BUT IT DOES HAVE ADMIRABLE ETHNIC COLOURATION
V155
THE COLOUR'S ACQUIRED
-IT STARTED OFF WHITE BUT BECAME THAT COLOUR BY CONSTANT SMOKING
Maurice Dodd
BY CRIKEY -THAT ARE DOING IT THE HARD WAY
MINE'S PER THE MANUFACTURER'S ORIGINAL SPECIFICATION

THIS ARE BEING A SOMEWHAT LETHARGIC FISH
SHOULDN'T IT BE MAKING IT'S WAY TO THE NEAREST AVAILABLE OCEAN?
Maurice Dodd
V156
WELL IT'S IN NO CONDITION TO DO THAT
IT'S BEEN SPLIT OPEN AND SMOKED FOR WEEKS OVER AN OAKCHIP FIRE
IN OTHER WORDS IT'S DEAD
-I'M NOT IN THE LEAST BIT SURPRISED

IT'S FOR THE GOOD OF YOUR NOSE
-IT ARE WAY BEYOND THE FLOWERS, GRAPES AND BEDSIDE-CHAT STAGE
WHY'RE WE VISITING A DEAD FISH?
V157

-IT'S TO GIVE YOUR NOSE A CHALLENGE-SOME ARDUOUS EXERCISE

WELL IF YOU THINK I'M USING MY NOSE FOR GRAVEDIGGING...
Maurice Dodd

COME BACK
I DON'T WANT YOU TO BURY THIS KIPPER - I WANT YOU TO SMELL IT
V158
Maurice Dodd
NOW LOWER YOUR NOSE TO IT
ARE YOU GETTING ANY SENSATION?
-A NUMBING PAIN IS SPREADING OVER ME FROM BEHIND
FROM BEHIND?
YES - YOU'RE TREADING ON MY TAIL!

ARE YOU FEELING ANY OTHER SENSATION?
NOW I'M NO LONGER STANDING ON YOUR TAIL
AH, YES - RELIEF - BLESSED RELIEF
Maurice Dodd
DAMME SIRRAH ARE YOU FEELING ANY SENSATION IN YOUR NOSE?
YOU'RE NOT THINKING OF STANDING ON MY NOSE?
V159
GURUUU - I'M FEELING A SENSATION IN MY TAIL AGAIN
GRRRRRR

NOW-CAN YOU SMELL ANYTHING?
NO
ENOUGH OF THIS BUFFOONERY- PUT YOUR NOSE TO THAT KIPPER AND BREATH DEEPLY
V160
WELL BREATH DEEPER -DEEPER
EVEN DEEPER
I'M BEGINNING TO THINK THERE'S LITTLE HOPE FOR YOUR NOSE
-AS A NOSE THAT IS
BUT AS A VACUUM CLEANER....
MD

I'LL HAZARD A LAST DESPERATE THROW IN AN ATTEMPT TO RESTORE YOUR OLFACTORY FACILITY, B.H.
AH-HERE WE ARE
THERE LURKS YONDER A RECLUSE GORGONZOLA OF UNCERTAIN AGE AND TEMPERAMENT TO MATCH
Maurice Dodd
HOW CAN ONE ACHIEVE CONTACT WITH THE CHURLISH CHEESE?
ER
-JUST WHISTLE
V161

WHISTLE?
ARE YOU TUGGING MY LEG, BOOT OLD CHAPS?
-ARE YOU SERIOUSLY INFORMING ME A CHEESE WILL EMERGE FROM THERE IF I WHISTLE?
V162
Maurice Dodd
WELL-NOT WITH ABSOLUTE CERTITUDE
-WE MAY HAVE TO BEAT IT OUT WITH A STICK!

ARE YOU SURE THE ANTIQUATED GORGONZOLA IS IN THERE?
Maurice Dodd
V163
WELL CAN'T YOU SMELL IT?
SNIFF
SNIFF
SNIFF

NO
SNIFF
SNIFF

-CAN YOU?

IT'S A DESPERATE GAMBIT BUT IF YOU CAN'T SMELL THAT GORGONZOLA THEN THERE'S NO HOPE FOR YOU
-SO WHISTLE AND LOWER YOUR SNOUT TO ITS LAIR- BUT PROCEED
♫
Maurice Dodd

GURUUUUUU
V164

IT BIT ME-IT BIT ME!
I HADN'T FINISHED HAD I?
...WITH CAUTION
GRRRRRRRRRRRRRRRRR

THAT ANTI-SOCIAL GORGONZOLA ACTUALLY BIT ME
WELL- IT HOLDS A GRUDGE AGAINST THE WORLD
YOU SEE-IT USED TO BE THE STAR TURN AT A GOURMET RESTAURANT
GRRRRRR
V165
-BUT IT GOT BEYOND ITSELF AND STARTED PESTERING THE CUSTOMERS
-FINALLY ASSAULTING THE NOTED FOOD FANCIER 'AGONY' ROONEY
'AGONY' ROONEY? WHAT A VERY PECULIAR NAME
OH, WELL -BEFORE THE ATTACK HE WAS KNOWN AS 'PAT'

YOUR ATTEMPTS AT RESTORING MY SENSE OF SMELLING HAVE BEEN A TOTAL FAILURE
NOT ONLY COULD I NOT SMELL THAT EVIL OLD CHEESE, BUT IT BIT ME!
AND I FAIL TO SEE WHY IT SHOULD BE BEARING A GRUDGE
ITS PREVIOUS BEHAVIOUR AT THE RESTAURANT CALLED FOR INSTANT DISMISSAL
Maurice Dodd V166
WELL-IT WENT A LITTLE BEYOND DISMISSAL
-THEY TRIED TO BURY IT-TWICE

WELL THIS HAS BEEN A FRUITLESS EXERCISE
ALL WE'VE LEARNED IS THAT YOUR NOSE IS COMPLETELY USELESS
YOU MIGHT AS WELL THROW IT AWAY
WHAT? AND WALK ROUND NAKED?
Maurice Dodd
NAKED?
YES-IF YOU REMOVED A DOG'S NOSE ALL THE SKIN WOULD SNAP BACK AND FALL ABOUT THE ANKLES
I'M FLABBER-GHASTED
EVERYBODY'S GHAST SHOULD GET A GOOD FLABBERING NOW AND AGAIN
V167

MY NOSE IS ALSO PART OF MY ESSENTIAL EQUIPMENT AS AN ACE REPORTER
QUICKS
FOR NOSING OUT THE TRUTH?
OH YOU HAVE NEVER SPOKEN A TRUER WORD
ESPECIALLY AFTER A SEARCHING INTERVIEW
Maurice Dodd
DURING WHICH I CAN BE SEEN TO BE MAKING DILIGENT NOTES
ON MY NOTE-PAD
-IT MAKES A VERY USEFUL RUBBER!
V168

IT HAVE JUST STRUCK ME!
I'M IN POSSESSION OF A RED-HOT HOLD-THE-FRONT-PAGE SCOOP-TYPE STORY
..."DEMENTED CHEESE SAVAGES ACE NEWSHOUND!"
YES, B.H.- BUT WILL ANYBODY BELIEVE IT?
PLEASE, BOOT, OLD CHAPS YOU'RE TALKING TO A PROFESSIONAL
NEVER MIND IF THEY BELIEVE IT- AS LONG AS THEY READ IT
V169
Maurice Dodd

CRUMBS BOOT, Y'VE BEEN GONE FOR AGES- WHERE'VE YOU BEEN?
V170
Maurice Dodd
-TIS A STRANGE TALE I RELATE- THOUGH NOT WITHOUT HUMOROUS ANECDOTE, IT ALL BEGAN WHEN...
...ROWF ROWF, ARF ARF ARF-ROWF ROWF...
OH WELL- IF YOU'RE GOIN' TO KEEP UP THAT STUPID BARKIN'-I'M OFF

BABY GRUMPLIN' WHAT HAPPENED AT THAT PLAY-SCHOOL?
we had finger-painting
Maurice Dodd
which, by natural progression, became elbow-painting, knee-painting, toe-painting nose-painting, ear-painting.......
but after that it got out of control
V171

-THEY WON'T LET ME ON A BUS WHEN I'M WITH YOU
WELL THAT WORKS BOTH WAYS YOU PLAINTFUL PUP
CRUMBS, BOOT, YOU'RE A BIT OF A LIABILITY

ALES
-THEY WON'T LET ME INTO THE PUB WHEN I'M WITH YOU
V172

AH-THERE YOU ARE DIRTY McSQUIRTY
POO-CRUMBS
LISTEN ALOYSIUS I'VE COME WITH A PETITION FROM THE REST OF THE SCHOOL
WOULD YOU CONSIDER TAKIN'A BATH?
MMM-W-E-L-L -ALRIGHT WELLINGTON -AS IT'S YOU...
-WHERE IS IT AND WHERE D'YOU WANT IT TAKEN TO?
Maurice Dodd V173

I'M NOT ASKIN' YOU TO TRANSPORT A BATH-TUB FOR ME
WHAT I'M SAYIN' IS WE WANT YOU TO HAVE A BATH
Maurice Dodd
WELL- THAT'S VERY KIND OF YOU

V174
-I COULD GROW FLOWERS IN IT

LOOK, DIRTY-McSQUIRTY-STOP AVOIDIN' THE ISSUE
WE WANT YOU TO GET INTO A BATH OF HOT WATER AN..
V175
WHAT?
WOULD YOU PLUNGE A GAINSBOROUGH INTO HOT WATER?
WOULD YOU IMMERSE A STRADIVARIUS IN FOAMING SUDS?
DO YOU WISH TO DESTROY MY PATINA?
ER...WELL HOW D'YOU FEEL ABOUT BEIN' GONE OVER WITH A BRUSH-AN'-DUSTPAN?
Maurice Dodd

YOU'RE BEIN' SILLY ALOYSIUS
-SOAP AN' WATER NEVER HURT ANYONE
V176

ENOUGH DESIST!
-DO NOT FLY IN THE FACE OF PROVIDENCE!

-IF GOD HAD MEANT ME TO HAVE BATHS HE'D HAVE SUPPLIED ME WITH CONSTANT HOT WATER

-END OF TERM COMIN' UP, BOOT TIME TO UNWIND, RELAX
V177

UNWIND? RELAX?

THE ONLY WAY TO RELAX YOU ANY MORE IS BY LETTING ALL THE AIR OUT!

I'M NOT GOIN' TO SAY ANYTHIN' ABOUT MY HOLIDAY OUTFIT THIS YEAR.
THEY ONLY GET SARKY
I'LL JUS' FLOAT PAST LIKE A VISION AN' WATCH THEIR EYES POP OUT
Maurice Dodd

DID YOU SEE WHAT I SAW?
YEA
BUT THEN AGAIN I 'AVEN'T BEEN TOO WELL LATELY
V178

WELL?
WELL?
SAY SOMETHIN'
OH, YEA MAISIE - WE'D JUS' LIKE TO SAY HOW SORRY WE ARE
BUT CHEER UP - THEY'RE PROBABLY WORKIN' ON A CURE FOR IT RIGHT NOW
FRONT
Maurice Dodd V179

AAHH-
WHADDA YOU
KNOW YOU
MORONS
THIS IS
THE LATEST
THING - A
PUFF-BALL
SKIRT
DI AN'
FERGIE
APPEARED
IN ONE
WE'RE
NOT A BIT
SURPRISED
THERE'S
ROOM ENOUGH
FOR BOTH OF
'EM
HA-HA-
HEEEE
HEE-HEE
HO-HO
HEEE
Maurice Dodd V180

YOU
IDIOTS - I'M
NOT SAYIN' DI
AN' FERGIE BOTH
GOT INTO THE
SAME SKIRT
THEY MADE
AN APPEARANCE
WEARIN' ONE OF
THESE PUFF-BALL
SKIRTS EACH
WELL IT'S
ALL RIGHT FOR
THEM
THEY'VE GOT
BODYGUARDS
HAR
HAR
HEEEE
HO-HO
HIC
HAAAA
Maurice Dodd V181.

OH I'VE HAD ENOUGH OF THIS
I'M GOIN' TO SIT UNDER THE TREE UNTIL YOU CLOWNS GET OVER YOUR SILLY FIT
HEEE
HO HO

BANG

CALL AN HEEEEEEE AMBULANCE
WHAT FOOL LEFT A RAKE UPWARD IN THE GRASS!
HUFF HUFF
HEE HEE
HAAA HO HO
V182

I CAN'T STOP THINKIN' ABOUT HOLIDAYS, BOOT
I GET VISIONS OF COBALT SKIES AN' GOLDEN SANDS
AN' WATERFALLS SHIMMERIN' DOWN TO INK-DARK LAGOONS
-INSTEAD OF WHICH WE'RE GOIN' TO ST MORIBUNDS AS USUAL
THAT'S THE BEST NEWS I'VE HEARD ALL WEEK
-I BURIED A BONE THERE LAST YEAR
V183

V184
bloop
it's coming 'round again new baby- and how i dread it
the heat- the sand- the flies
-the long marches across an alien landscape
i'd do anything to avoid going
glop
-i thought i'd found a way-only to have mi hopes dashed
i've still got to go on holiday
berk
-they told me i'm too young to join the legion

IF THERE'S ONE THING I CAN'T STAND IT'S PACKIN'
-THERE'S NEVER ENOUGH ROOM AN' EVERYTHIN' TAKES UP MUCH MORE SPACE THAN YOU'VE ALLOWED FOR
THE THINGS YOU WANT TO GET AT ON THE WAY ALWAYS WORK THEIR WAY TO THE BOTTOM
V185
AN' WHEN YOU'RE PACKED TIGHT YOU FIND YOU'VE LEFT OUT THE THING YOU WANTED MOST
YOU'RE NOT FOOLING ME
-YOU'RE WORKING YOURSELF UP TO TACKLING IT IN ONE FRENZIED WHIRL OF APATHY
Maurice Dodd

I'M SURE MARLON WON'T MIND IF I ADD A LITTLE BIT TO HIS PILE
Maurice Dodd
I DON'T S'POSE HE'LL EVEN NOTICE
COME TO THINK OF IT HE NEVER NEED KNOW
COME TO THAT WHERE IS MARLON?
MARLON? YOO-HOO MARLON IT'S TIME TO GO
I'M TRYIN' TO GO, MAISIE
BUT THIS FLAMIN' PACK...
IT SEEMS T'BE GETTIN' 'EAVIER BY THE MINUTE
V186

YOU'VE BOOKED ON A COACH?
IT'LL COST A FORTUNE!
NO-NO, THEY'RE DIRT CHEAP SINCE PRIVERTISATION
V187
WELL IN THE CIRCUMSTANCES I THINK IT'S ROBBERY AT ₤2·50 EACH!
WEST COUNTRY FLYER
MD

WELL THANKS, MAISIE – THANKS A HEAP
– SO WE GOT A REFUND –BUT WE ALSO GOT TURNED OFF THE COACH
WELL I DON'T CARE – I'M ENTITLED TO COMPLAIN ABOUT BAD MANNERS
ALL RIGHT– BUT PIGS AREN'T NOTED FOR OFFERIN' LADIES THEIR SEATS
OINK
OINK– OINK
V188
MD

I THINK WE'RE LOST
I'VE GOT A COMPASS – CAN ANYBODY READ A COMPASS?
I CAN O'COURSE
I MEAN POO–WHO CAN'T READ A COMPASS?
WOT IT SAYS IS...
– MERIDIAN COMPASS CO., SHEFFIELD, ENGLAND
V189
Maurice Dodd

WELL, NOW I KNOW WE'RE LOST—I DON'T RECOGNISE ANY OF THIS
HEY— THERE'S A SIGN HERE SAYIN' St. MORIBUNDS 'ARF A MILE
WE SHOULD'VE BEEN THERE BY NOW
YEA— WE'VE BEEN GOIN' FOR HOURS
I DON' UNNERSTAN' IT
V190
—AN' I EVEN TURNED THE SIGN TO POINT IN THE WAY WE'RE GOIN'

WHERE ARE WE?— WE DON'T KNOW!
WHERE ARE WE GOIN'? WE DON'T KNOW!
AN' IT'S ALL YOUR FAULT, MARLON
WHAT KIND OF A NIDIOT ARE YOU?
ER...
THE LOST KIND?
V191

'ERE - WHY DON'T WE GET OLE BOOT TO FIND THE WAY?
YEA - DOGS ARE S'POSED T'BE GOOD AT THAT
YEA, C'MON BOOT, SHOW 'EM HOW IT'S DONE
V192
WOT'S 'E DOIN'?
HE'S LIMBERIN' UP
WOT'S 'E DOIN' NOW?
HE'S FINDING THE SCENT
AN' NOW?
I DUNNO
IT'S WHAT'S KNOWN IN THE TRADE AS PLAYING FOR TIME

DON'T STAN' THERE LOOKIN' DAFT, BOOT - FIND THE WAY FOR US
- TRUST YOUR INSTINCTS. FOLLOW YOUR NOSE
OH VERY WELL THEN
V193
WELL, THAT WAS ONE OF THE SILLIEST SUGGESTIONS I'VE HEARD IN A LONG, LONG TIME -

LOOK AT THAT STUPID DOG!
WE SENT HIM TO FIND A WAY FOR US AND WHAT DOES HE DO?
–'E GETS 'IS NOSE STUCK IN A TREE
YOU SHUTTUP – BOOT'S A VERY SMART DOG, BOOT IS
HE MADE A MISTAKE THAT'S ALL
HE PROBABLY THOUGHT IT WAS A 'PHONE-BOX
WELL YOU CAN'T GET MUCH SMARTER THAN THAT – CAN YOU?
Maurice Dodd V194

HE-E-E-A-V-E
I'LL CLIMB IN AN' PUSH FROM INSIDE
HO!
WELL THAT'S IT
YEA, LET'S GET GOIN'
THERE'S ONLY ONE SNAG
I'M STUCK
MD V195

NOW WELLIN'TON'S STUCK IN THE TREE - HOW COULD HE DO IT?
AN' WHAT'RE WE GOIN' TO DO?
TELL YOU WOT LET'S THROW A BUCKET OF 'OT OIL IN
WHAT A STUPID SUGGESTION
V196
FOR ONCE MARLON - I'M INCLINED TO AGREE WITH WELLIN'TON
THAT WAS A STUPID SUGGESTION
WHERE ON EARTH COULD YOU GET A BUCKET OF HOT OIL AT THIS TIME OF DAY?

RIGHT ONCE AGAIN- THE OLE H-E-E-AVE

HO!

A GUMBOOT..
ALL WE'VE MANAGED TO PULL OUT IS WELLINGTON'S GUM-BOOT
TELL YOU WOT
-LET'S GO AHEAD WITH THE GUMBOOT AN' MAYBE THE REST OF 'IM WILL FOLLOW.LATER
V197

WELLIN'TON'S WELL AN' TRULY STUCK IN THAT TREE
HOW'RE WE GOIN' TO GET HIM OUT?
I'VE GOT A NIDEA
I'LL GET SOME DRY STICKS AN' WE'LL SET FIRE TO IT
AAGH
MARLON - A BRILLIANT SOLUTION
BY APPLYIN' PSYCHOLOGY HE WAS OUTA THERE LIKE A SHOT
I CAN'T SEE ANY SMOKE
YEA? ...FUNNY THAT
Maurice Dodd
V198

WROWF WROWF
-A-LOTTA USE SENDIN' THAT STUPID DOG TO FIND THE WAY
YEA-'E'S JUST AS LOST AS WE ARE
HANG ABOUT-HE'S FOUND SOMETHIN' -HE'S POINTIN'
YEA-I REMEMBER THIS LANE
'RAY-'E'S CRACKED IT!
WELL DONE, BOOT
YOU'VE PROVED YOU'VE THE INSTINCTIVE ABILITY TO FIND A TRAIL
I RATHER THINK IT HAS MORE TO DO WITH MY ACQUIRED ABILITY TO READ
SAINT MORIBUND'S ¼ MILE
Maurice Dodd
V199

V200
WELLIN'TON -WHAT MAKES YOU THINK YOU C'N FIND THE PLACE WE CAMPED LAS' TIME?
LOOK, MAISIE, I KNOW WHAT I'M DOIN' SO STOP TICKIN' AN' –
AAAAGH
I THINK I'VE FALLEN DOWN A 'OLE
THINK? WHADDAYA MEAN, THINK, MARLON - AREN'T YOU **SURE**?
'OW CAN I BE **SURE**? IT'S PITCH BLACK DOWN 'ERE!

RIGHT LET'S GET THE TENT UP AN' GET A GOOD NIGHT'S KIP
I DON'T THINK THIS IS THE RIGHT PLACE. THE GROUND'S VERY SOFT
LOOK, MAISIE, I KNOW EX'ACLY WHERE WE ARE. SHUT UP AN' BANG THE PEGS IN
V201
AT THE RISK OF BEIN' CALLED CRITICAL -WOULDN'T YOU SAY IT'S A **TRIFLE** DAMP?
CRUMBS, MAISIE -YOU'RE IN THE COUNTRY. Y'GOTTA EXPEC' A HEAVY DEW
Maurice Dodd

OH YOU BIG'EAD WELLIN'TON. YOU BIG'EAD YOU
V202 Maurice Dodd
YOU WOULD'N' LISTEN TO ME WOULD YOU -YOU KNEW WHERE TO PITCH THE TENT DIDN'T YOU?
AN' WHERE WAS THAT? -IN THE SEA
WATCH Y'SELF, MAISIE, IF YOU'RE NOT CAREFUL YOU'LL BE PUTTIN' YOUR FOOT IN IT
ME? - PUTTIN' MY FOOT IN IT?
I DON'T WANNA HEAR ANY MORE ADVICE ON ANYTHIN' FROM YOU
HAVE IT Y'R OWN WAY

'RAY
WHOO
HAAA
Maurice Dodd
-just one moment maisie
is this what's known as *having fun?*
YEA
WEYHEY
i just thought i'd ask
YAHOO
WHEE
V203

AAAGH
A SPIDER
A GREAT WHITE WOOLLY SPIDER SHOUTED B-A-A-A AT ME!
V204

B-A-A-A
THAT'S NOT A SPIDER — IT'S A SHEEP

–THE LENGTHS THEM DIABOLICAL SPIDERS WILL GO TO!

LOOK, MAISIE, THAT'S NOT A SPIDER — IT'S A SHEEP, Y'GET WOOL FROM IT
V205

B-A-A-A
Y'WOULDN' CATCH ME WEARIN' SPIDER'S WOOL
POO

SO — YOU'RE A SHEEP ARE YOU?
IT SO HAPPENS I'M AN OLD ENGLISH SHEEP-DOG
WHAT D'YOU THINK OF THAT?
B-A-A-A
B-A-A-A
B-A-A-A
B-A-A-A
B-A-A-A
I'M GLAD I NEVER PURSUED IT AS A CAREER
V206

LOOK, BABY GRUMPLIN' — I WANT A BIT OF A SNOOZE AN'A SUNBATHE
— AN' I DON'T WANT YOU BOTHERIN' ME
SO SHOVE OFF AN' MAKE YOUR OWN AMUSEMENT
i'm a little rain-cloud floating in the blue
i'm going to rain all over you
well i thought it was amusing
V207

THERE THAT PROVES IT
SPIDERS!
MILLIONS'N MILLIONS OF BIG WOOLLY SPIDERS
SHEEP, MAISIE—WE KEEP TELLIN' YOU THEY'RE SHEEP
YEA? WELL IT'S A WELL-KNOWN FAC' THERE'S TWO MILLION SPIDERS IN EVERY ACRE OF FIELD
—CAN YOU SEE ANY OTHERS?
V208

WELL IF THEY'RE SPIDERS WHERE ARE THEIR WEBS?
SPIDERS HAVE WEBS
V209
ER...
WEBS?
ER...
OH IT'S NO USE ARGUIN' WITH THE LIKES OF YOU
ANYBODY WHO DOESN'T KNOW THE DIFFERENCE BETWEEN A SPIDER AN' A DUCK...

IT'S TIME FOR MY IN-DEPTH SCRUTINY OF THE OLD ROCK-POOL
...AND EVERY YEAR ABOUT THIS TIME BROTHERS THERE APPEARS AN AWESOME PHENOMENANA
THE EYEBALLS-IN-THE-SKY
HEY — WHY'RE YOU PICKIN' MY POCKETS ?
'OW DARE YOU — I'M A FREE-LANCE TAX COLLECTOR
A SPECTECACKLE OF SUCH NUMBING NUMENOSITY THAT YOU UNWORTHY REPROBATES MUST **PREPARE** YOURSELVES
THE SPIRIT MOVES ME TO ORDER YOU DOWN ON YOUR KNEES
I OFTEN 'AVE A RENT REPROBATE
YOU MEAN THAT COLLECTOR 'OO ACCEPTS FAVOURS IN LIEU OF MONEY
V210
KNEES ARE... ER... UM ...AH... STAND BY FOR A FLASH ANNOUNCEMENT
THE SPIRIT HAS CHANGED HIS ORDER TO STAND ON YOUR HEADS!
OI — 'ANG ABOUT — WHAT'RE KNEES ?

PUT YOURSELVES IN A STATE OF TRANQUILITY, CONTEMPLATION AND INNER CLEANLINESS BY STANDING ON YOUR HEADS
AND PREPARE YOURSELVES FOR THE EYEBALLS-IN-THE-SKY
IF I SUFFERED FROM CONTEMPLATION THAT'S THE LAST THING I'D WANT TO DO
YEA — IT DON'T GIVE GRAVITY A CHANCE
SHUTTUP AN' DO WOT THE LEARNED AN' MYSTICAL IDIOT SAYS
V211
GET DOWN — GET DOWN YOU CRETINOUS CRUSTACEANS
STAND ON YOUR **OWN** HEADS — NOT EACH OTHER'S
AAGH
NO — BUT IF YOU 'UM IT I'LL BUSK IT
D'YOU KNOW YOU'VE GOT YOUR FOOT IN MY EYE ?
HOOP-LA
CRIPES — THAT'S MORE OF A SITTIN' TENANT THAN A JOKE
YEA — 'E GETS IT IN EVERY YEAR
CRIPES — SOME PEOPLE ARE NEVER SATISFIED
SO YOU'VE READ MY LETTER TO MARJ PROOPS

V212
THE EYEBALLS-IN-THE-SKY WILL HERALD THE END OF THE WORLD!
OR SOMETHING OR THE OTHER
BUT IT'LL FRIGHTEN THE LIVES OUT OF YOU — YOU TEETERING TRANSGRESSORS
BONK
I'VE GOT A NEADACHE
BONK
YOU SHOULD'VE TOLD ME BEFORE WE STARTED
I'LL BET IT WON'T BE THE OTHER
OH — THERE'LL BE NAILING AND WASHING OF TEETH AND —WHAT'S THAT BANGING NOISE?
OUCH
BONK
SHRIEK
'OW COULD I — YOU'D STUFFED YOUR SOCKS IN MY MOUTH
WHAT'S GOING ON DOWN THERE?
— STANDING ON THEIR HEADS AND BONKING TOGETHER
WHAT?
I DIDN'T SAY ANYTHING ABOUT ENJOYING YOURSELVES
THEY'RE TRYING TO FOLLOW YOUR ORDERS, YOUR VERBOSENESS
BONK
BONK
I DON'T THINK WE'LL TAKE THIS UP ON A REGULAR BASIS
IT'S GIVEN ME A NEW RESPECT FOR AUSTRALIANS

CEASE THIS RAMPANT RIBALDRY
I SAID STAND ON YOUR HEADS—THAT'S ALL
I WANT NO BANGING, BONKING, GIGGLING, GROPING, LEERING, LECHING, FUMBLING, TUMBLING...
BONK
BONK
BONK
I DON'T KNOW 'ARF THEM THINGS —I'M TAKIN' NOTES
I WONDER WHERE WE C'N GET THE INSTRUCTIONS?
AH— THIS LOOKS LIKE THE POOL— I'LL DIP DOWN FOR A DECKO
V213
...VULGARITY, HILARITY, RUDENESS, LEWDNESS, SMUTTYNESS, RUTTYNESS, HANKY OR PANKY
SHRIEK
THEY'RE HERE!
IT'S TRUE!
OH, WELL —MAYBE ON SATURDAYS AND BANK HOLIDAYS
GROAN
SOB
SWOON
WHIMPER

I WONDER WHAT THEY'RE UP TO ?
ALL THE CRABS ARE MILLING ABOUT DOWN THERE
THIS IS THE POOL RIGHT ENOUGH
V214

. . . AND TO PREPARE FOR THE COMING OF THE EYEBALLS-IN-THE-SKY
THEY'RE HERE—THEY'RE HERE—LOOK UP!
AIEE!
I'VE BEEN VINDICATED!
I DON'T WANNA HEAR ABOUT YOUR OPERATION —I'M OFF
I'VE BEEN PARALYSED
I'VE BEEN RIPPED OFF
I'VE BEEN TRANSFIXED
IT WAS AN ACCIDENT—MY CLAW CAUGHT IN THE ELASTIC
I'VE BEEN, AN' I WISH I 'ADNT

PONDER ON THE MANIFESTATION OF THE EYEBALLS-IN-THE-SKY MY BRETHREN
OOH
AAAH
OOH, BEE, I FIND MYSELF BREATHING IN SHORT PANTS
THEY'RE MUCH TOO TIGHT BY THE SOUND OF IT
GET OFF YOU CREDULOUS CRACKPOT OR YOU'LL BE PONDERING ON THE MANIFESTATION OF A Dr.MARTIN'S IN THE FUNDAMENT!
GASP—WHO ARE YOU ?
LOOK OUT—IT'S A FUNDAMENTALIST
THEY CAN'T TOUCH YOU FOR IT
V215
ONE WHO'LL PROVE THE EYEBALLS TO BE A MERE CHIMERA—I SPEAK IN THE NOBLE NAME OF SCIENCE
HOW DO I KNOW YOU'RE A SCIENTIST ?
WHAT'S A CHIMERA ?
A POSH NAME FOR A SHIFT
'COS I GOT A WHITE COAT AIN' I ?
GULP
I SHOULD'VE 'AD MORE RESPEC' FOR MY BRUVVER
'E WAS TAKEN AWAY BY TWO SCIENTISTS

SCIENCE WILL PROVE THE EYEBALLS TO BE NOTHING BUT A PRODUCT OF MASS HYPNOSIS
—BY SENDING AN ANTI-GRAVITY PROBE UP INTO THE GREAT UNKNOWN
FOOLS— YOU'LL REND THE FABRIC OF THE UNIVERSE
I DON'T BELIEVE IN 'IPNOSIS
I DO— OUR AUNT 'AD IT DONE— SHE WENT AS STIFF AS A BOARD
IT CAME IN VERY 'ANDY FOR THE IRONIN'
WHEN SHE DIED WE MADE 'ER INTO A BOOKSHELF
V216
IN OTHER WORDS—A LOBSTER-BALL (BRING IT ON MEN)
—WHICH WE'VE RE-NAMED THE CRABMOGLOBE
DOOM— DOOM
I'VE ALWAYS WANTED TO GO TO A LOBSTER-BALL
WELL I WOULD'N' WANT IT TO COME TO ME
RE-NAMED? THAT'S A RELIEF— I DREAD TO THINK WHAT MIGHT'VE FOLLOWED
—PROBABLY A HIGHLY ENRAGED LOBSTER

ONCE RELEASED THE CRABMOGLOBE WILL RISE RAPIDLY BEYOND THE REACHES OF THE POOLIVERSE
TAKING WITH IT A VOLUNTEER— HANGING ON FOR DEAR (DAMN— WHERE ARE MY NOTES)
RISING RAPIDLY? SOUNDS LIKE A YUPPY
—I 'AD ONE O' THEM— 'E 'AD LOVELY FLOPPY EARS AN' A CUTE LI'L WET NOSE
'E USED TO CREEP INTO MY BED AT NIGHT
V217
—I MEAN A BRAVE CRABRANAUT WHO'LL RIP THE VEIL FROM THE SO-CALLED EYEBALLS-IN-THE-SKY
AIEEE
Y' VE GOT IT WRONG— THAT WAS A LITTLE DOG
DOES A DOG SELL STOCKS AN' SHARES?
COR— I C'N THINK OF BETTER THINGS TO RIP THAN VEILS
YOU'RE WASTIN' YOUR TIME DEARIE— I'M A FRESH-AIR FIEND

RIGHT — I WANT ONE VOLUNTEER
ONE BRAVE SOUL WILLING TO VAULT INTO THE DARK NIGHT OF DANGER — RISKING HIS ALL
— SOMEBODY FULL OF THE STUFF HEROES ARE MADE OF
I'M VOLUNTEERIN' — FOR THE 100 METRE DASH
I'D GO—BUT THE REST OF ME VOTED AGAINST IT
I'VE AN URGENT APPOINTMENT WITH MY W.C.
WELL **I'M** NOT... HEY...
MY CLAW'S CAUGHT IN THE NETTIN'!
I CAN'T LET GO-O-O
V218
THEY DON'T MAKE HEROES LIKE THEY USED TO
THEY CAN'T GET THE STUFFING YOU KNOW
HELP

SOMETHING SEEMS TO BE AFOOT DOWN THERE
THERE'S A CRAB CLINGING TO A GLASS BOWL
V219
AND HE'S HEADING MY
WAY!

GRRRRRRR
AAAGH

IT'S HORRIBLE — HORRIBLE
THERE'S SOMETHIN' HUGE AN' HAIRY — AN' IT GROWLS
CRIPES!
DON'T TELL ME MY **EX-WIFE'S** OUT THERE

YOUR WIFE WAS HUGE AND HAIRY — AND SHE GROWLED ?
YEA — SHE WAS MY KIND OF WOMAN
— SHE COULD HAVE HER WAY WITH ME ANY TIME
— NO MATTER HOW HARD I FOUGHT
V220
SHE MUST'VE BEEN A BIT OF A (HEE HEE) LOOKER
I DON'T KNOW — I NEVER SET EYES ON HER
I COULDN'T YOU SEE — WE LIVED IN A PITCH-BLACK COAL-HOLE
A COAL-HOLE ? WHATEVER FOR ?
— SHE WAS VERY SHY

FOOL— STANDING THERE DRIBBLING ABOUT YOUR EX-WIFE, WHAT'S HAPPENED TO THE EYEBALLS-IN-THE-SKY ?
DON'T DISTRACT ME — IF I'VE FOUND HER AGAIN — I MUST CONTACT HER
D'YOU THINK THIS COULD DEVELOP ?
ONLY IF YOU EXERCISE IT REGULARLY
HOW DID YOU LOSE HER IN THE FIRST PLACE ?
I TOLD YOU WE LIVED IN A COAL HOLE AND I COULDN'T EVEN SEE HER
I DON'T KNOW
WELL ONE DAY I COULDN'T FEEL HER— SHE JUST WASN'T THERE
AT FIRST I THOUGHT SHE'D JUST BECOME COLD AND UNRESPONSIVE
THEN I REALISED— FOR FOUR NIGHTS I'D BEEN JOLLYING UP A LUMP OF COAL
THIS HAS ALL THE MAKINGS OF A SORDID BEST-SELLER
CAN I HAVE THE SERIAL RIGHTS ?
YOU MEAN — YOU WANT A TUMBLE IN THE CORNFLAKES ?
V221

FLEUR
SPEAK TO ME
MY SWEET SWEET FLEUR— REMEMBER THOSE NIGHTS IN THE COAL-HOLE ?
BY THE LORD HARRY— THERE'S A CRAB DOWN THERE WAVING AT ME AND BLOWING BUBBLES
—OBVIOUSLY EXPECTS ME TO RESPOND
V222

CRIPES
AAIEE
RROWF
RROWF
I THINK I'VE GOT THE WRONG WOMAN
UNLESS KING KONG 'AD A NABIT OF 'ANGIN' ROUND COAL-'OLES DRESSED IN DRAG

RROWF
RROWF
IT'S THE END OF THE WORLD THANKS TO YOU, YOU COSMIC CLOWN
V223
YOU'VE RENT THE FABRIC OF THE POOLIVERSE AND WE'RE BEING FLOODED WITH THE DREADED RROWF
Y'MEAN— YOU WEREN'T INSURED ?
I HOPE YOU'RE COVERED FOR THIS — BUT YOU WON'T LIVE TO COLLECT IT
STAND BACK — I'M A BLACK-BELT IN ORIGAMI
THUD
BIFF
GOUGE
WELL— THAT'S THAT— NOT THAT I CAN EVER MAKE ANY SENSE OF IT
I'LL LEAVE THEM IN PEACE FOR ANOTHER YEAR
DOES IT ALWAYS END LIKE THIS ?
YES —I DREAD THESE W.I. MEETINGS
BIFF
THUD
CRUNCH

IT'S TIME TO START FOR HOME- WE'RE WELL OVERDUE AT SCHOOL
YEA - C'MON, MARLON-Y'GOTTA MAKE A MOVE
LOOK- TWITCHIN' YOUR TOES AN' WIGGLIN' YOUR EARS WAS NOT WHAT WE HAD IN MIND
Maurice Dodd
V224

OH WELL, (SIGH) THAT'S IT
IT'S GOODBYE TO ALL THIS FOR ANOTHER YEAR
oh yes goodbye rocks- in- sea, goodbye stones-on- beach
goodbye sandwiches with real sand in them
goodbye wasps, goodbye flies
goodbye nettles goodbye thistles
goodbye cow- pancakes goodbye ...
Maurice Dodd V225

WELL,BOOT-IT'S BACK TO SCHOOL WITH A VENGEANCE - THIS IS GOIN' TO BE A CRUCIAL YEAR
I'VE GOT TO GIRD UP THE WHATSITS-BITE THE BULLOCK-GRIND TO THE NOSESTONE
IT'S SHOULDERS TO THE WHALE AN' ALL CISTERNS GO
AN' WHAT'S MORE BLAH BLAH DRONE DRONE BLAH
IN THE MEANTIME I TAKE IT, WE'RE AT THE PLANNING STAGE
Maurice Dodd
V226

WELL HERE I GO, BOOT-FIRST DAY BACK AT SCHOOL
ALL SET FOR A YEAR OF INTELLECTUAL ACHIEVEMENT-I'M GOIN' FOR THE GOLD
-HANG ABOUT I'D BETTER CHECK THAT I'VE GOT EVERYTHIN' I NEED
PAPER-DART, GOBSTOPPER, BEETLE IN MATCHBOX, FUNNY NOSE, BEANO, WATER SQUIRTER....
Maurice Dodd
V227

SCHOOL
CRUMBS - I 'ATE SCHOOL
IT'S A LIBERTY SO IT IS - ANOTHER YEAR'S 'ARD
SCHOOL MAKES MY BRAIN 'URT
OH COME ON, MARLON WE'RE GOIN' T'BE LATE
CRUMBS, MAISIE - I'M GOIN' AS FAST AS I CAN - AIN'T I?
THAT'S TRUE - THAT'S VERY TRUE
'SPECIALLY SINCE YOU'RE WALKIN' BACKWARDS
V228
Maurice Dodd

'LO, MARLON - 'LO, MAISIE
CRUMBS - WE'RE WELL LATE FOR SCHOOL
DON'T I KNOW IT
-GIVE US A PUSH!
V229
Maurice Dodd

SCHOOL
CRUMBS -SCHOOL
IF I DIDN'T HAVE TO GO TO SCHOOL I COULD BE OUT ER, THINGYIN' AN' ENJOYIN' MYSELF
Maurice Dodd
OH STOP BEIN' STUPID, MARLON, Y'GOTTA GO TO SCHOOL
D'YOU WANNA BE AN IGNORANT FAILURE ALL YOUR LIFE?
W-E-L-L NO
V230
-ONLY FOR THIS PART OF IT

HEY, BOOT, I'M HOME
LET JOY BE UNCONFINED
IT WAS HARD THE FIRST DAY BACK BUT AT LEAST I STARTED WITH THE RIGHT ATTITUDE
READY TO GET IN THERE AN' SOCK IT TO 'EM
EAGER TO WORK-FIRED BY AMBITION
V231
I WONDER WHERE IT ALL WENT?
Maurice Dodd

BABY GRUMPLIN'
MUM SAYS I C'N TAKE YOU TO THE FLICKS THIS AFTERNOON- THERE'S A DISNEY SHOWIN'
one moment maisie - i must consult mi diary.
Maurice Dodd
V232
12·30 pm fill brolly with frozen peas
1pm-place beetle in bath
1-30pm spread glue on loo-seat
2pm mmm..
i'm afraid i can't accompany you-i'm fully booked
....slip spider into nightie while maisie's at the flicks

WHAT'RE Y'READIN' ABOUT, FISCAL?
READING?
-I'M ABOUT TO CONSULT FILOFAX
MY PRIME SOURCE OF INFO NECESSARY FOR SURVIVAL IN THE BIG-BANG ERA
-DEFINING THE BOTTOM LINE ON BROKERS LAFER CURVES ETC
V233
I DON'T KNOW HOW ANYONE CAN GET ON MARKET-WISE WITHOUT FILOFAX -KNOW WHAT I MEAN?
OW YEA. RIGHT, NICE ONE, MAGIC, LIKE
WELLIN'TON- WHO'S PHYLO FAX?
Maurice Dodd

I SAID WHO'S PHYLO-FAX?
UM... LET'S SEE NOW... A POP-STAR?
A HAIRDRESSER?
A SINGIN' DETECTIVE! A TRAMPOLINE TUNER?
A HAMBURGER DESIGNER? OH I DON'T KNOW -I GIVE IN
FISCAL YERE SAID PHYLO FAX REFINES THE BOTTOMS OF A LINE OF BROKERS WIV A LOOFA
IN WHICH CASE I CHANGE MY PLEA FROM 'DON'T KNOW' TO 'DON'T WANT TO KNOW'
Maurice Dodd
V234

HEY - FISCAL, WHAT'S THIS TALE YOU'VE BEEN TELLIN' MARLON?
ABOUT THIS PHYLO FAX WHO'S GOIN' 'ROUN' REFININ' BROKERS BOTTOMS?
IT'S NOT A WHO IT'S AN IT
FILOFAX YOU KNOW-THE COMPENDIUM OF BIZ-FAX OF VITAL INFO FOR THE MARKET-WISE EXEC
EVERYONE WHO'S ANYONE HAS GOT ONE OF THESE
V235
YOU MEAN, YOU HAVEN'T GOT ONE?
OH I WOULD'N' SAY THAT
I'D SAY DAM' AN' CRIPES - AN' CURSES, AN' OOORGH - BUT I WOULD'N' SAY THAT
MD

DISASTER. BOOT. DISASTER GRIEF AN' HUMILERATION
EVERYBODY AT SCHOOL'S GETTIN' A FILOFAX
ANYBODY WHO'S ANYBODY IS GOIN' TO HAVE A FILOFAX
I'M NOT GOIN' TO HAVE A FILOFAX
I CAN'T AFFORD A FILOFAX
OH (GULP) THANKS BOOT
BUT I DON'T THINK A CARDBOARDBOXOFAX IS GOIN' T'PUT ME WITH THE 'IN' CROWD
V236
Maurice Dodd

A FILOFAX?

CRUMBS, MAISIE - WHAT C'N YOU DO WITH A FILOFAX?

A SIMPLE EXPLANATION WOULD'VE SUFFICED
Maurice Dodd
V237

DIRTY McSQUIRTY!
YOU'VE GOT A FILOFAX?
WHATEVER DO YOU KEEP IN IT?
ITEMS OF CONSIDERABLE INTEREST
- SUCH AS 'BRACHINUS CREDITANS' AN' 'PTEROSTICHUS MADIDUS'
THE ONLY THING IS...
-IT DOES TEND TO FLATTEN THEM
V238
Maurice Dodd

HAVE YOU GOT ANYTHIN' OTHER THAN SQUASHED BEETLES IN YOUR FILOFAX?
OH-YES SOMETHING QUITE UNIQUE

-LOOK

WELL WHO ELSE D'YOU KNOW'S GOT SUCH AN EXTENSIVE COLLECTION OF STAINS?
V239

BABY GRUMPLIN'! EVEN YOU'VE GOT A FILOFAX
WHAT ON EARTH DO YOU PUT IN IT?
some extremely important names and addresses wellington
-cuddy bunny toy co., pull-along ducks inc., maximum chaos jokes ltd., king-kong-o-grams...
keeny-meeny disruptive appliances (suppliers to the s a s), rentathug...
NEVER KNOWN A FILOFAX TO GO SO RAPIDLY DOWNHILL
V240

CRUMBS MARLON (SIGH) EVEN YOU'VE GOT A FILOFAX- WHAT D'YOU KEEP IN IT?
INIT? WELL... NUFFIN'-I DIN'T KNOW IT WAS FOR KEEPIN' THINGS IN
WELL IT'S OBVIOUS-AS THE NAME IMPLIES
FILE-O' FAX - IT'S FOR-KEEPIN' FACTS IN. SEE?
OW...YEA... WELL I KNEW THAT
♪
ER...
I S'POSE YOU WOODEN KNOW WHERE I C'N GET 'ALF-A-DOZEN FAX'S, CHEAP-LIKE?
FRONT
V241

CRUMBS- NOW EVERYBODY'S GOT A FILOFAX
EXCEPT ME
I CAN'T FACE IT- I'LL BE A NOBODY WITHOUT A FILOFAX
GET A GRIP WELLIN'TON-WHAT DO YOU CARE- YOU DON'T CARE DO YOU?
AS LONG AS YOU'RE NOT SEEN IN PUBLIC WITHOUT A FILOFAX YOU DON'T
MD
V242

STATIONERY CUPBOARD
CRUMBS- IF Y'HAVEN'T GOT A FILOFAX YOU'RE NOTHIN' -A NOBODY
IS SOMEBODY IN THERE?
WHO'S IN THERE?
NOBODY
OH COME NOW-YOU CAN'T BE NOBODY- EVERYBODY'S SOMEBODY
V243
HUH- I'LL BET YOU'VE GOT A FILOFAX

COME ON, WELLIN'TON - COME OUT OF THE CUPBOARD
YEA-WE'RE YOUR FRIENDS
WE WON'T HUMILERATE OR DEGRINATE YOU-JUS' 'COS YOU HAVEN'T GOT A FILOFAX
YEA- WE WON'T DISAPARGE OR OSTRICH-EYES YOU
MOSTLY 'COS WE CAN'T PERNOUNCE ANY OF THEM THINGS
BUT JEER, WE C'N PERNOUNCE JEER
V244

ALL MY LIFE I'VE MOILED AN' TOILED AN' HOW DO I END UP?
-AS THE ONLY KID IN THE ENTIRE SCHOOL WHO HASN' GOT A FILOFAX
THERE MUS' BE SOME WAY OF GETTIN' A FILOFAX
-IF YOU HAD ANY GO IN YOU-YOU'D GO OUT AN' BITE AN ADVERTISIN' EXECUTIVE
V245

METHINKS YOUNG WELLINGTON'S OBSESSIVE DESIRE FOR A FILOFAX HAS ADDLED THE POOR PUP'S BRAIN
Maurice Dodd V246
FANCY HIM SUGGESTING I OBTAIN ONE BY ASSAULTING AN ADMAN
HAS HE ANY CONCEPTION OF WHAT AN ADMAN TASTES LIKE?
A SMOOTH VELVETY COATING OVER A COMPLETELY NUTTY INTERIOR
EASILY BROKEN UP BY THE THREAT OF LOSING AN ACCOUNT
I REQUIRE... SOMETHING MEATIER TO CHEW ON
BUT I DOUBT THERE'S MUCH CHANCE OF FINDING A NAVVY WITH A FILOFAX

AH-B.H. (CALCUTTA) FAILED
Maurice Dodd
DO YOU PERCHANCE KNOW THE LOCATION OF A GOOD CONDITION FILOFAX?
INDEED SO -WE ARE HAVING ONE AT THE WEST CROYNGE CLARION & DUBIOUS ADVERTISER
AS WELL AS MANY OTHER MODERN INNOVATIONS
IS THERE ANY CHANCE OF MY...ER.. BORROWING IT?
GOODNESS GRACIOUSNESS NO - IT ARE PERFORMING A VITAL FUNCTION
-IT ARE PROPPING UP A LEG OF THE NEWSDESK
V247

WHY'S YOUR PAPER'S FILOFAX PROPPING UP THE NEWS DESK?
THE DESK IS SUFFERING FROM HAVING ONE LEG SHORTER THAN ITS OTHERS
CAUSED BY OUR SOMEWHAT VOLATILE EDITOR CHEWING IT!
YOUR EDITOR CHEWED A DESK LEG? WHATEVER FOR?
-HE'D RUN OUT OF CHAIRS
Maurice Dodd
V248

IN ASKING WHY YOUR EDITOR CHEWED A DESK LEG I WAS NOT CONDUCTING A SURVEY ON ALTERNATIVE COMESTIBLES
I WAS CURIOUS AS TO HIS MOTIVE
HE WERE IN A TIZZ BECAUSE WE WERE SCOOPED ON A RED HOT STORY
TO WIT- CHEEKY GRAN FLAUNTS FRILLIES IN TESCO'S
AND WHY DID SHE DO THAT?
WELL, THERE WAS SOME EMBROIDERY INVOLVED - ON THE STORY, NOT THE KNICKERS
THE SHOCKED SHOPPERS WERE BOGGLED BY THE BLOOMERS WHEN THE POOR OLD DEAR TRIPPED OVER A TROLLEY
Maurice Dodd
V249

AH-TATTY OLD BITT
WHOOPSH
I S'POSE YOU WOULDN'T HAVE A FILOFAX ABOUT YOUR PERSON?
FILOFAXSH? YOU C'N SEARCH ME
YOU DON'T MEAN-YOU'VE GOT ONE?
GOT ONE? I DON'T EVEN KNOW WOT IT ISH
I JUSHT ENJOY BEIN' SEARCHED
V250
Maurice Dodd

HEY, BOOT-I'VE HAD A NIDEA
IT'LL BE MY BIRTHDAY (AN' DAY OF NASHNUL REJOICIN') SOON
OCTOBER 25TH, SHOULD ANYONE WISH TO TAKE NOTES
I'M STARTIN' A CAMPAIGN TO GET A FILOFAX AS A PREZZY
MAYBE I SHOULD WRITE A SLOGAN
LEMME SEE...
FILOFAX MAKES THE HEART GROW FONDER?
FAINT HEART NEVER WON FAIR FILOFAX?
A FILOFAX IN NEED...? TROUBLE IS SOMEBODY'S ALREADY THOUGHT OF THEM
OK-SO WHAT? I'D HAVE THOUGHT OF 'EM TOO BUT I WAS TOO YOUNG AT THE TIME
V251
MD

I'M RUNNIN' OUT OF TIME FOR MY BIRTHDAY 'FILOFAX' APPEAL
AN' I GOTTA THINK OF A CONVINCIN' ARGUMENT
Maurice Dodd
V252
NOW TAKE EVOLUTION- WE START OFF AS A BLOB AN' END UP WALKIN' ERECT-WITH A FILOFAX
-AN' IS THERE ANY ONE OF YOU WHO'D REFUSE TO THROW A FILOFAX TO A DROWNIN' MAN?
WHAT IS THIS LIFE IF FULL OF CARE. WE HAVE NO TIME TO STAN' AN' STARE-AT OUR FILOFAX?
YEA-'TIS BETTER TO GIVE THAN TO RECEIVE - ESPECIALLY A FILOFAX
OH (SIGH) I DUNNO-I'M BEGINNIN' TO WONDER IF THE SUBTLE APPROACH IS GOIN' TO WORK
LICK LICK

EVERY BRITISH HEART SHOULD LEAP AT THE MENTION OF AGINCOURT
-WHERE A HANDFUL OF BRAVE BRITS DEFEATED THE FLOWER OF FRENCH SHOVELRY
-ON OCTOBER THE 25TH
- WHICH ALSO HAPPENS TO BE MY BIRTHDAY
IMAGINE THE SCENE- THE BRITS STAND READY- A SMALL DEFIANT BAND
-IN MASSED RANKS THE FRENCH MOVE MENACINGLY FORWARD
-THE BRITS RAISE THEIR FILOFAXS...
V253
-WELL THEY WERE CHECKIN' THAT THEY WERE AT THE RIGHT FIXTURE
MD

WELLINGTON-
SINCE YOU
WANTED ONE SO
BADLY- I'VE
BROUGHT YOU
A FILOFAX
CRUMBS,
THANKS-THANKS
A HEAP,
ALOYSIUS
I HAD TO
SEARCH HIGH
AND LOW FOR
THIS
OH? ARE
THEY IN SHORT
SUPPLY?
V254
I'LL SAY-
YOU DON'T FIND
MANY ON A
RUBBISH-TIP
Maurice Dodd

Y'MEAN-
Y'GOT THIS
FILOFAX FROM
THE RUBBISH-
TIP?
YES-IT'S
MY BIRTHDAY
PRESENT TO
YOU

IT'S A BIT
SPOTTY AN'...ER..
PUNGENT
OOH-YES-
ISN'T IT JUST

V255
-I HAD A
TERRIBLE STRUGGLE
PARTING WITH IT!

OK-SO MY FILOFAX CAME OFF THE RUBBISH-TIP-IT'S STILL A FILOFAX
HI THERE - FISCAL YERE - LOVELY DAY FOR A FILOFAX
Maurice Dodd V256
I HAPPEN TO HAVE ONE
I JUS' THOUGHT I'D MENTION IT
IN PASSIN'
I ONLY ASKED IF YOU HAD THE INVESTMENT PORTFOLIO TO GO WITH IT

AN' I'M NOW ONE OF THE 'IN' CROWD
EVEN IF MY FILOFAX DID COME FROM THE RUBBISH-TIP, I'VE GOT ONE
OH - HI-THERE, MAISIE
Maurice Dodd V257
I'M TAKIN' MY FILOFAX FOR A WALK
I MEAN POO-WHO HAS'N' GOT A FILOFAX?
PRACTICALLY EVERYBODY AS A MATTER O' FAC'
IT JUS' IS'N' THE 'IN' THING ANY MORE
-I THREW MINE ON THE RUBBISH-TIP

BOY AM I FED UP– NOBODY'S EVER BEEN FEDDER UPPER THAN I AM
AT LAST I GET A FILOFAX AN' NOBODY WHO'S ANYBODY'S GOT ONE ANY MORE
Maurice Dodd V258
WHEN THE 'IN' CROWD WERE IN I WAS OUT
AN' NOW I'M IN – THE 'IN' CROWD ARE OUT
WHAT'M I GOIN' TO DO WITH MY LIFE?
I'M A FAILURE– A REJECT
OH DEAR -THE LAD'S IN DIRE NEED OF A LIFEBELT
I THINK I'LL MAKE MYSELF A SNACK
CANCEL THE LIFEBELT – WE'VE SETTLED FOR A SAUSAGE SARNIE

THE EPISODE OF THE FILOFAX SHOULD BE A LESSON TO US, BOOT
IT'S USELESS TO KEEP STRIVIN' AFTER EVERY PASSIN' FANCY
Maurice Dodd
V259
FOOLISH TO WANT SOMETHIN' JUS' 'COS SOMEBODY ELSE HAS IT
THE WISE MAN'S CONTENT WITH HIS LOT AN' NOT FOREVER YEARNIN' FOR..

YOU HAVEN'T BEEN LISTENIN' HAVE YOU?

TATTY OLDBITT!
'ULLO SHAILOR (HIC)
GISH A KISH
`PON MY SOUL, MADAM- YOU GAVE ME QUITE A TURN
S'FUNNY, DEARIE, I'VE NO RECOLLECTION OF THAT
YOU MUST'VE SNUCK-UP ON ME WHILE MY ATTENTION WAS DIVERTED
V260
Maurice Dodd

LISH'N, SHAILOR -I'M NOT IN THE 'ABIT OF ENCOURAGIN' GENTS TO SNEAK INTO MY BOOD-WAR AN'...
DAMME, MA'AM, I DON'T EVEN KNOW WHERE YOUR BOUDOIR IS
OH
-'ANG ABOUT- I'VE GOT A BLUEPRINT AN' DIRECTIONS SOMEWHERE DOWN 'ERE
Maurice Dodd
V261

LISTEN, TATTY- SINCE I'VE NO INTENTION OF GOING THERE
I DO NOT WISH TO KNOW WHERE YOUR BOUDOIR IS
OH, CAN'T WAIT A? THE IMPATIENT TYPE (HIC)
V262

I'M YOURS, SHAILOR - I'M YOURS

UNHAND ME, MADAM - DESIST!
C'MON, SHAILOR - GISSA BREAK - I'VE BEEN DOIN' A 'EAVY TOUR OF DUTY - MINESWEEPIN'
MINESWEEPING? IN THE GULF?
NAH - POMPEY
HOW CAN YOU CARRY OUT MINESWEEPING IN PORTSMOUTH?
WELL JUST BEFORE CLOSIN' TIME YOU MAKE A SWEEP OF THE PUBS PATRONISED BY THE BOYS IN BLUE
AN' WHEN YOU FIND A JOLLY JACK TAR 'OO'S A BIT UNDER THE INFLUENCE
LIKE FALLIN' OFF 'IS BAR-STOOL
YOU RUSH IN AN' SHOUT 'E'S MINE!
Maurice Dodd V263

WHEN YOU SAID YOU'D BEEN MINESWEEPING, I THOUGHT YOU'D BEEN ENGAGED ON HAZARDOUS DUTIES...
... NOT PICKING UP SAILORS IN PORTSMOUTH
'AZARDOUS? 'AZARDOUS? WHAT DO YOU KNOW ABOUT 'AZARDOUS?
'AVE YOU EVER TRIED TO GET A MATELOT OUT OF A PUB?
Maurice Dodd
V264

ANYWAY-I 'AVE DONE REAL MINESWEEPIN', I WAS 'SPECIALLY TRAINED...
... FOR DEALIN' WITH BOOZEMINES
BOOZEMINES?
YEA - A DIABOLICAL DEVICE INVENTED BY AN ENEMY WHO KNEW OF THE NAVY'S PARTIALITY TO RESTORATIVE CORDIALS
THEY SUBMERGED QUANTITIES OF 'GENUINE FARM'OUSE 'XTRA STRENGTH OLDE ENGLISH SCRUMPY -TYPE CIDER (CONCOCTED IN CAMDEN TOWN)'
OH... AND THAT WOULD TEAR THE BOTTOM OUT OF A SHIP?
BELIEVE YOU ME - THAT STUFF WILL TEAR THE BOTTOM OUT OF ANYTHIN'
V265 Maurice Dodd

HOW DID THEY DEAL WITH THE LETHAL HIGHLY ALCOHOLIC BOOZEMINES?
NO-THEY TOWED ME
I TAKE IT THEY TOWED A PARAVANE
USIN' THE PRINCIPLE DEVELOPED FOR MAGNETIC MINES
WHERE THEY PASS SOMETHIN' METALLIC LIKE A CROWN-CORK OVER THE TOP
AH, YES - AND WHEN IT PASSES OVER, THE MINE BOBS UP
YEA 'CEPT IN THE CASE OF A BOOZEMINE - I BOBS DOWN
Maurice Dodd
V266

HAVING LOCATED THE HIGHLY ALCOHOLIC BOOZEMINE HOW DID YOU DEAL WITH IT?
WELL THE FIRST STAGE IS CIRCUMVENTIN' THE OUTRAGEOUS CHARGE
IS IT REALLY CALLED AN OUTRAGEOUS CHARGE?
WELL WOT WOULD YOU CALL IT?
V267
-THERE'S OVER A 100% MARK-UP ON THEM THINGS -PLUS VAT AN'...
Maurice Dodd

WHAT I WANT TO KNOW IS-HOW D'YOU RENDER A BOOZEMINE SAFE?
BY WITHDRAWIN' THE EXPLOSIVE CONTENTS
Maurice Dodd V268
I SUPPOSE THAT CALLS FOR EXPERTISE AND SOPHISTICATED EQUIPMENT
OOH-YEA, A BUNG-BORER AN' A LONG RUBBER TUBE
OH- AN' A MARASCHINO
A MARASCHINO? WHAT WAS THAT FOR?
YOU'RE FORGETTIN' AIN'T YOU? I'M A LADY
I COULDN' DRINK ALL THAT LOT WITHOUT A CHERRY

YOU SAT ON THE SEA-BED AND QUAFFED THE ENTIRE CONTENTS OF A BARREL OF BOOZE?
YEA-THEN I 'AD TO STRUGGLE TO THE SURFACE
THEN STRUGGLE ON BOARD SHIP
THEN STRUGGLE WITH THE SEAMEN, STRUGGLE WITH THE BOSUN, STRUGGLE WITH THE FIRST-MATE
AN' END UP STRUGGLIN' WITH THE CAPTAIN
I DUNNO' WOT WAS WRONG WIV THEM (SIGH) I NEVER USED TO 'AVE TO DO ALL THAT STRUGGLIN'
-THE NAVY'S NEVER BEEN THE SAME SINCE THEY GAVE UP THE GROG RATION
V269
Maurice Dodd

I SHOULD'VE THOUGHT THERE'D BE SOME RECOGNITION OF YOUR GALLANT SERVICE ON THE HIGH SEAS
WELL THERE WAS TALK OF A GRATEFUL NATION AWARDIN' A DECORATION AN' A STATE BANQUET
OH? FROM WHICH QUARTER?
FROM THIS QUARTER
I KEP' SPREADIN' IT ABOUT- BUT NOTHIN' CAME OF IT
Maurice Dodd
V270

I TAKE IT YOU'VE NOW LEFT THE MINESWEEPER
I RECEIVED A MEDICAL DISCHARGE
MEANIN'- THEY THREW ME OFF THE SHIP
- SUCH WAS THE NATURE OF MY AFFLICTION THEY WOULDN'T HAVE ME ON BOARD
DRINKIN' BARREL AFTER BARREL OF GENUINE FARM'OUSE 'XTRA-STRENGTH OLDE ENGLISH SCRUMPY TYPE CIDER WAS WOT DID IT
-IT GOT ME IN THE END
WHAT EXACTLY WAS THE NATURE OF YOUR AFFLICTION?
I TOLE YOU - IT GOT ME IN THE END
V271
Maurice Dodd

C'MON, SHAILOR-EENUFF OF THIS CHIT-CHAT
GIVVA GIRLA GRAPPLE
OOOH I LOVE IT WHEN THEY SHTRUGGLE
GET OFF, MADAM-DESIST
GOODNESS GRACIOUSNESS
THIS CONDUCT IS MOST DISGUSTINGLY REPREHENSIBLE -AND IN PUBLIC TOO
WELL WHAT'RE YOU STANDING THERE FOR THEN?
I'M FORMING A QUEUE
V272

HELL'S TEETH-GET OFF ME, MADAM

-GET OFF
GOODNESS GRACIOUSNESS

YOU ENGLISH ARE VERY WASTEFUL
THERE'S YEARS OF GOOD WEAR AND TEAR LEFT IN THAT WOMAN
V273

PARDONING ME-
AM I ADDRESSING TATTY OLDBITT (THE SAILOR'S FRIEND?)
YOU MUS' BE THE TALL MAHOGANY-TINTED TYPE THE GIPSY TOLE ME TO EXPEC'
BY JINGO!
YOU MUST HAVE EYES IN THE BACK OF YOUR, ER, HEAD
OR IS IT WHAT'S KNOWN AS SECOND SIGHT?
NO - IT'S WOT'S KNOWN AS A 'OLE IN THE BOTTOM OF THE BIN
V274
MD

ARE YOU DOING ANYTHING FOR DINNER TONIGHT?
EATIN'- WIV ANY LUCK

I'M IN A POSITION TO OFFER YOU AN ACTION-PACKED VINDALOO
A POSITION IN AN ACTION-PACKED WINDY-LOO?
YOU CERTAINLY KNOW THE WAY TO A GIRL'S 'EART YOU SHMOOTH-TALKIN' ROGUE
I'M YOURS, SHAILOR - I'M YOURS
Maurice Dodd
V275

KNOW WHAT, BOOT-I'VE DECIDED TO BECOME A WRITER
WHAT KIND OF A WRITER THOUGH-THAT'S THE THING
IT NEEDS A LOT OF THINKIN' ABOUT
IT'S A DIFFICULT DECISION
I MEAN SHALL I BE A SPACEMAN WRITER OR A COWBOY WRITER OR A NENGINE-DRIVER WRITER OR...
V276
Maurice Dodd

WHAT'RE Y'DOIN', WELLIN'TON?
FRONT
I'VE DECIDED TO BECOME A WRITER
WRITIN' A STORY
NOW THERE'S A NIDEA-I THINK I WILL TOO
OH COME ON, MARLON-YOU C'N HARDLY WRITE YOUR OWN NAME
V277
FLAMIN' CHEEK-I'LL SHOW YOU IF I C'N WRITE MY OWN NAME OR NOT-
M.. A...
M... A...
OH IT'S ALL VERY WELL TO CRITICISE
Y'COULD AT LEAST OFFER TO 'ELP

Y'VE BEEN WORKIN' FOR A COUPLE OF HOURS OVER THERE, MARLON
HAVE YOU WRITTEN A STORY YET?
V278
OOH-YEA
WELL.. A TITLE
-VERY NEARLY
IT'S CALLED BLOODSTAINS ON THE CARPET... AN' THE WALLS.. AN' JUS' ABOUT EVERYWHERE IN FAC''
I'M JUS' WRITIN' IT DOWN NOW
ER...
-ALMOS'
HOW D'YOU MAKE A 'B'?

HEY, BOOT-
I'VE JUS' WRITTEN MY FIRST STORY -LISTEN
AHEM-
THE THING IN THE ATTIC'...
'ONCE THERE WAS A THING IN THE ATTIC'...
'I DISCOVERED IT'...
'AAAAGH - GRAB-BITE - CRUNCH-BLOOD -I WISH I HADN'T!'
V279

WELL IT'S A SHORT STORY

HEY, BOOT - I'VE RE-WRITTEN 'THE THING IN THE ATTIC'

IT NOW GOES-'ONCE THERE WAS A THING IN THE ATTIC'....
V280

'I DISCOVERED IT...'
'AAAGH - GRAB-BITE - CRUNCH!...'

'IT WAS QUITE TASTY, REALLY'

ANOTHER RE-WRITE ON 'THE THING IN THE ATTIC', BOOT

IT NOW GOES...'ONCE THERE WAS A THING IN THE ATTIC...'

'IT LAUGHED AN' LAUGHED AN' LAUGHED AN' LAUGHED'

IT'S A HUMOROUS STORY, SEE?
V281

THE WORLD OF ANDY CAPP
37
EVERY CHRISTMAS - TRIES TO CAUSE A ROW SO HE WON'T HAVE TO BUY ME A PRESENT.
AT YOUR NEWSAGENT TODAY
UK £2.25